PROFITABLE CONSERVATION

Business Strategies That Boost Your Bottom Line, Protect Wildlife, and Conserve Biodiversity

MARK ASPELIN

Gypsy Road Publishing, Sandia Park, NM 87047

Printed in the United States of America

First Printing 2018

978-0-9970879-2-5 (print)

978-0-9970879-3-2 (e-book)

Editing, interior design, and production by Joanne Shwed, Backspace Ink, www.backspaceink.com

Cover design by Miladinka Milic, www.milagraphicartist.com

Front cover Adobe Stock photo credit: Coral Reef Photo by vlad61_61

I dedicate this book to my parents, who provided me with so many opportunities to encounter wildlife and experience nature throughout my childhood.

I also dedicate this book to my son Erik, whose love for animals is infectious and a joy to witness. I hope your passion for animals continues to be a source of inspiration and happiness throughout your life.

Finally, I dedicate this book to the countless people who are committed, in their own way, to protecting wildlife and biodiversity. Thanks for all that you do to make the world a better place.

Table of Contents

Acknowledgments

The people who have contributed to this book are too numerous to count. I have experienced 25+ years of interactions with teachers, coworkers, mentors, scientists, family, friends, and acquaintances. Thousands of books and articles have provided new ideas, and hundreds of nature documentaries from greats like Sir David Attenborough helped fuel my fascination and passion for the natural world.

Two people played a particularly important role in inspiring me to take the plunge into the world of biodiversity and wildlife conservation: Edward O. Wilson and George Archibald. While in grad school in 1992, Wilson's book, *The Diversity of Life*, caught my attention and planted the idea that I should dedicate my career to the conservation of biodiversity and wildlife. A short time later, George Archibald gave me my first taste of on-the-ground wildlife conservation while working at the International Crane Foundation, which he founded. I had the opportunity to work on-site in Baraboo, Wisconsin, at the captive breeding facility for endangered cranes, and then in the field in the western highlands of Kenya. These two amazing experiences and learning opportunities formed the foundation of my understanding of what effective, on-the-ground conservation really looks like.

When it comes to writing this book, I would like to thank two people: Jane Atkinson and Joanne Shwed. Jane played an important role in convincing me to focus on the topic of profitable conservation rather than go off in another direction; Joanne's outstanding design and editing assistance created a final product that is infinitely more polished and professional.

Finally, I would like to thank you for reading this book! I hope you find it thought-provoking and a valuable use of your time. Better yet, I hope you find a few ideas that you'll experiment with to help protect biodiversity and wildlife in your corner of the world.

E. O. Wilson and Mark Aspelin at Biodiversity Days, March 2017

List of Acronyms

ACROS	Asian Crossroads Over the Sea
AI	artificial intelligence
BISON	Biodiversity Information Serving Our Nation
CESMO	Corredor Ecológico de la Sierra Madre Oriental
CO_2	carbon dioxide
CO_2e	carbon dioxide equivalent
DfE	Design for the Environment
EDRR	early detection and rapid response
EPR	extended producer responsibility
FY	fiscal year
GIS	Geographic Information Systems
GRI	Global Reporting Initiative
HACCP	Hazard Analysis and Critical Control Point
HIPPO	habitat destruction, invasive species, pollution, human overpopulation, and overharvesting
HP	Hewlett-Packard
HVAC	heating, ventilation, and air conditioning
ICF	International Crane Foundation
IFC PS6	International Finance Corporation Performance Standard 6
IIRC	International Integrated Reporting Council
IoT	Internet of things
IPM	integrated pest-management [strategy]
ISO	International Organization for Standardization

IT	information technology
IUCN	International Union for Conservation of Nature
LCA	life-cycle assessment
LED	light-emitting diode
LEED	Leadership in Energy and Environmental Design
MBA	Master of Business Administration
NFWF	National Fish and Wildlife Foundation
NGO	nongovernmental organizations
NOx	nitrogen oxide
PC	personal computer
PPA	power purchase agreement
PVC	polyvinyl chloride
REACH	Registration, Evaluation, Authorization and Restriction of Chemicals
REDD+	reducing emissions from deforestation and forest degradation, plus the role of conservation, sustainable management of forests, and the enhancement of forest carbon stocks
RedE	Resource Efficiency Deployment Engine
RoHS	Restriction of Hazardous Substances
ROI	return on investment
SASB	Sustainability Accounting Standards Board
SEC	[U.S.] Securities and Exchange Commission
SLOSS	single large or several small [habitats]
SOx	sulfur oxide
VOC	volatile organic compound

Introduction

"If you think you're too small to make a difference, try sleeping in a closed room with a mosquito."
—African proverb

Reality Check in Africa

When it comes to tackling the challenging issue of biodiversity and wildlife conservation, there are several effective approaches to consider, such as legal action, governmental policy, scientific research, and grassroots activism. However, there's another angle that sometimes gets overlooked: creating incentives for corporations to play a more active role in protecting wildlife and biodiversity. The link between business and biodiversity may not be immediately obvious, but, after reading this book, you'll have a solid understanding of why and how businesses are an important part of the solution.

My journey into the intersection of business and biodiversity began over 25 years ago, but I remember it like it was yesterday. I had completed an undergraduate degree in biology from the University of Notre Dame (Notre Dame, Indiana) and a master's degree in biology from Creighton University (Omaha, Nebraska). After traveling the world for an extended period, I landed a position as an aviculture intern at the International Crane Foundation (ICF) (Baraboo, Wisconsin). After several months of working with the captive breeding program for endangered crane species, I received a phone call from George Archibald, ICF's founder and president. George asked if I would be interested in working on a crane-conservation project in East Africa.

After picking up my jaw from the floor, I answered, "Yes!"

The next thing I knew, I was on a plane bound for Kenya.

Shortly after arriving to work as a conservation biologist in the rural communities surrounding Saiwa Swamp National Park in western Kenya, a tribal leader asked, "Can you help us develop income-generating projects for our community?"

At the time, my answer was a polite form of, "Heck no!"

After all, I was clueless about business, and I was hoping to keep it that way. I was an idealistic college grad with no intention of working in a "soul-sucking" job, toiling away in some lifeless cube farm in a large company. No, thanks. That was not for me.

However, the longer I worked in rural Africa, the more I saw the need to learn about business. The biology part seemed straightforward: We wanted to protect gray-crowned cranes and the wetlands on which they depended. The tricky part was that our conservation goals were not always aligned with what the local community needed to make ends meet. The local population required access to the basics: food, fuel, and medicine. Given that the average farmer only earned about US$ 250 per year,[1] these basics were hard to come by. Instead, it was common practice to enter nearby Saiwa Swamp National Park to poach animals, strip bark from trees for medicinal purposes, and gather wood to use as cooking fuel.

After seeing the reality of day-to-day life in Africa, it was hard to find fault with the people who participated in these illegal activities. I was surrounded by people with malaria, cholera, and dysentery, with no money to buy medicine. Given the realities of our budget and resources, I could see no effective way to separate the wildlife-conservation work from the community-development work. If we could provide the local community with the ability to develop sustainable sources of income—and access to clean water, food, fuel, and medicine—we could enlist the community's support to protect wildlife and biodiversity.

The tribal leader's words echoed in my mind: "Can you help us develop income-generating projects for our community?"

After one month, I changed my answer: "Yes, I will try."

I didn't realize it at the time, but I was taking my first steps on a long journey to uncover ways to make conservation profitable.

From my tent in rural Kenya, I applied to several business schools that seemed like a good fit for an outlier like me. Later that year, I received an acceptance letter from the Master of Business Administration (MBA) program at the

University of Texas. I was off to Austin to complete an MBA with concentrations in natural resource and environmental management and operations management. Of course, I didn't even know what operations management was when I arrived in Austin, and it was a steep learning curve.

Now, 20 years later, I've had the opportunity to experience more than my fair share of cube farms and *Office Space* movie moments in a wide variety of large corporations. The amazing part is that I eventually found that I enjoyed a lot of it! I've met many terrific people on a journey that has taken me all over the globe.

My resume provides plenty of laughs for any job recruiter. Here's the embarrassingly long list, in case you're interested:

- The Coca-Cola Company, Environmental Programs Manager
- The Nature Conservancy, Conservation Biologist
- Intel Corporation, Business Process Re-engineering Specialist
- Fidelity Investments, Senior Operations Project Manager
- KPMG, Consultant—Environmental Management Practice
- Sandia National Laboratories, Senior Project Manager—Environmental Planning and International Security
- Environmental Resources Management Inc., Environmental Consultant
- DaVita HealthCare Partners, IT Project Manager
- Molina Healthcare, Senior Project Manager
- D. Pennington & Associates (Transportation Planning), Senior Environmental Planner
- The International Crane Foundation, Aviculturist and Conservation Biologist

Putting it mildly, it's not the resume I had envisioned when I first graduated from college!

What have I learned from this kaleidoscope of experience? For starters, it shattered my former, naïve perception of corporations. Most companies want to "do the right thing" when it comes to the environment, but they want to do it in a way that enables the organization to meet its specific mission and goals. Of course, one of those goals is to make a profit or else the company wouldn't be in business in the first place. However, if you propose solutions that protect the environment and add value to the business, then most senior leaders will be eager to listen.

My experience taught me how to get things done in a corporate setting. Whether attempting to sell senior management on a new idea or taking a project through its life cycle, there's a right and a wrong way to approach these efforts in the business world. Talking to senior management about the importance of an environmental issue will fall flat if it's not backed up with a thoughtful proposal, including action steps that the company should take to address the issue, a strong value proposition that describes how those actions will help the business grow and improve, and a clear definition of how to measure success.

I learned that many of the greatest environmental gains come from nonenvironmental jobs. The best improvement ideas often come from teammates with job descriptions that don't mention the word "environment." It's not necessary for these teammates to have an interest in environmental issues. An environmental challenge can be framed from the perspective of improving efficiency, reducing costs, and minimizing waste. By doing so, a variety of people will be happy to use their detailed knowledge of processes and products to identify new opportunities that are good for business. Many of these ideas are also good for the environment.

The same is true for tackling environmental challenges in society. For real progress on an issue, it's generally wise to avoid alienating half the room with political trash-talking or industry-bashing; instead, think of how you can bring a broad spectrum of stakeholders to the table. There are many passionate conservationists on both sides of the aisle; they just approach the issue from a different angle.

Finally, I learned that corporate sustainability is not rocket science. While the underlying science may be complicated, practical application of conservation concepts is relatively simple. The hard part is choosing the best path forward for your organization, convincing senior management to approve and fund conservation initiatives, and getting your organization aligned and excited to carry out the plan.

What You'll Learn from This Book

In this book, I focus on a key idea, which I call "profitable conservation," meaning any action that benefits wildlife, biodiversity, and business. A long list of actions may meet that criteria; however, as the late, great, personal development guru Jim Rohn used to say, "There are always a half-dozen things that make 80% of the difference"[2] for any area of life. In this book you'll learn the half-dozen things that businesses can do that make 80% of the difference when it comes to benefiting wildlife, biodiversity, and the bottom line.

The "half-dozen things" I selected are based on my work experience as a conservation biologist and corporate environmental manager. I've also added some insights from the numerous environmental lectures and conferences that I've attended over the years, including target audiences that wore tie-dyed and flannel shirts, animal costumes, camouflage, and tailored suits. I feel comfortable in any of those settings and have learned that each of these perspectives represents a valid and important piece of the conservation puzzle.

While each audience may approach things from a different angle, they're all interested in knowing the answer to the question, "What can we do to help protect biodiversity and the environment?" However, different audiences will take actions that are aligned with their expertise. For example, government agencies will create incentives and regulations to steer efforts in a direction that helps them move forward with their important conservation work; nonprofit organizations create conservation strategies and solicit donations from individuals and businesses to fund their important conservation work; corporate-sustainability managers develop a business case and pitch it to senior management to get approval and funding to move forward with their important conservation work.

This book will tackle, head-on, the big question with which corporate managers all over the world typically struggle: "What environmental investments are worth pursuing for *my* organization?"

Of course, the answer to this question is the ever-popular, "It depends."

The answer depends on a variety of factors including company strategy, pressure from customers and competitors, and the regulatory environment. To help you answer this question for your organization, we'll look at success stories from a variety of corporations and industries and discuss the key factors that you should consider in determining if a strategy is a good fit for your business.

While biodiversity and wildlife conservation may not be a top-of-mind priority for many companies today, it will become more and more of a concern in the years to come. Biologists are alerting us to the fact that we're experiencing major losses of wildlife habitat and biodiversity throughout the world, and they're taking steps to minimize the damage. Corporations, on the other hand, are expanding operations and hoping to grow. It's just a matter of time before the actions of corporations and biologists collide. Corporations will face increasing stakeholder scrutiny and pressure to do their part to protect our planet's biodiversity and wildlife. This is already happening in some industries, and this trend will continue to increase as we witness the extinction of more and more species.

As a conservation-biology and corporate-sustainability geek, I'm passionate about biodiversity conservation and the role of corporations in protecting biodiversity. Corporations play a critical role in biodiversity conservation. After all, corporations own a significant chunk of the land throughout the world, and their operations and purchasing decisions have direct and indirect impacts on our planet's biodiversity and limited natural resources.

This book attempts to bridge the gap between the efforts of corporations and the efforts of biologists to protect our planet's wildlife, biodiversity, and natural resources. Fortunately, conservation versus profit is not a zero-sum game where the winner takes all. There are many win-win scenarios, which are good for business (e.g., reduced costs, reduced risk, and increased profits) and good for biodiversity (e.g., healthy species, populations, and ecosystems).

I'll provide a clear action plan on what corporations can do to help protect biodiversity and wildlife as well as guidance on how you can implement those strategies in your organization.

Content and Format of This Book

This book is divided into three parts:

- In Part 1 (Chapters 1 and 2), we'll look at the corporate and biologist perspectives on the topic of biodiversity and natural-resource management, including a primer on corporate environmental-management strategies to help you better understand how companies manage natural resource and environmental issues. Then, we'll put on our conservation-biology hat and see how biologists view the topic of biodiversity conservation and discuss the all-important business case for biodiversity and natural-resource conservation.
- In Part 2 (Chapters 3 through 7), we'll dive into various profitable-conservation strategies that corporations can choose, which have the potential to benefit business and biodiversity, along with guidance on how to implement these strategies. Each chapter will close with a list of action items to help you identify your best course of action for that topic.

- In Part 3 (Chapters 8 through 12), we'll walk through four case studies that feature businesses from a variety of industries. This will give you a better idea of how other companies approach and practice biodiversity and wildlife conservation. These companies aren't perfect, but they provide a good representation of the broad spectrum of profitable-conservation approaches that companies are taking to protect wildlife and biodiversity. Then we'll close with a call to action that applies to each us, as individuals, regardless of what we do for a living.

As you've probably figured out by now, I've written this book in a conversational style, which I hope you'll find easier and more enjoyable than a traditional textbook. To increase the odds that you'll finish this book, I've also decided to keep it short and to the point. I won't try to impress you with technical jargon, complex theories, and academic references. Instead, I'll provide just enough information to help you identify action steps that make sense for your business along with key points that may help you sell your ideas to senior management. If you walk away with one to three ideas with which you'll experiment in your organization or your own life, then I'll consider this book to be a fantastic success!

As someone who's been in the trenches, implementing corporate-sustainability and conservation-biology programs and projects, I'll stick to what I know best: sharing best practices and ideas on how to develop and implement profitable-conservation strategies for your organization.

Well, enough of my yacking. Let's dive into the world of profitable conservation. Whether your experiments succeed or fail, I would love to hear from you (mark@profitableconservation.com) to learn about your efforts to protect our planet's biodiversity and wildlife.

Introduction Endnotes

1. Personal discussions with local farmers, Kenya, 1996.
2. Jim Rohn, *Excerpts from the Treasury of Quotes* (Lake Dallas: Jim Rohn International, 2010), 20.

PART 1

A Primer on Green Business Strategies and Biodiversity Conservation

Chapters 1 and 2 provide a primer on green business strategies and biodiversity conservation, which will serve as a foundation for the profitable-conservation strategies covered in Parts 2 and 3.

CHAPTER 1

A Primer on Green Business Strategies from a Business Perspective

"A man generally has two reasons for doing a thing: one that sounds good, and a real one."
—J. P. Morgan

Overview of Green Business Strategies

I know that the above quote from J. P. Morgan sounds a bit cynical; however, when it comes to corporate environmental strategy, there's a lot of truth to it. Yes, a handful of companies are guided by a passionate commitment to environmental conservation—Patagonia, Method (now part of Ecover), and Seventh Generation—that inextricably links their businesses with the environment. The leaders of these companies might even prefer to go out of business rather than be a poor steward of the environment and are convinced that they will be handsomely rewarded by their customers. Of course, these inspirational, high-minded companies are not the norm. Most companies are in business to make a profit, and their commitment to environmental protection is a fickle one that depends on company performance and profits.

While there may appear to be many environmental-management strategies that companies can adopt, it boils down to seven basic strategies regardless of your industry or business. Some companies choose to adopt one of these seven strategies while others implement multiple strategies in parallel. This chapter will provide a whirlwind tour of each of the seven corporate environmental-management strategies along with some guidance to identify which strategy or combination of strategies is appropriate for your business.

Strategy #1: Core Business Competencies

With this simple strategy, you choose to meet the basic requirements of the vast array of environmental regulations and focus your attention on the core competencies of your business. This strategy may sound appealing if you run a small business or work for a larger company in an industry with minimal environmental impacts. However, by pursuing this approach, you'll likely miss out on significant opportunities to improve your company's bottom line through cost-saving and revenue-generating opportunities.

Strategy #2: Tithing

A popular choice among companies, the basic gist of a tithing or a charitable-giving strategy is like Strategy #1. You focus on running a high-performing business while staying in compliance with environmental regulations. However, you take the additional step of donating a portion of your company's profits or resources, usually in the form of volunteer work, to support worthwhile causes and nonprofit organizations aligned with your company's mission and vision. Tithing may sound like a weak, standalone strategy, but it can do a lot of good, depending on the environmental issue of concern.

Let's take the issue of biodiversity conservation as an example. From a conservation-biology perspective, the best things that we can do to protect biodiversity on this planet include the following ambitious goals:

- Set aside about half of the Earth's surface (including oceans) as a natural reserve, undisturbed by man, following the guidance of renowned biologist Edward O. Wilson in his book *Half-Earth: Our Planet's Fight for Life*. The goal is to protect large tracts of land in biodiversity hotspots, protect key marine waters, and string together patches of core habitat in the industrialized world with wildlife corridors and restored habitat. By protecting half of the Earth, with a focus on high-priority areas, scientists estimate that we can protect 85% of the species that exist today.[1]

- Be good stewards of the land outside of natural reserves, which may include a variety of goals such as zero-carbon emissions, zero waste, 100% renewable energy use, the planting and protection of native vegetation, and the removal of invasive species.

A tithing strategy fits very well with the first bulleted item above, perhaps more so than any other strategy geared towards the conservation of biodiversity. Why? When it comes to identifying the best things that we can do to protect biodiversity, the most effective approach is to set aside large chunks of land to manage as preserves in biodiversity hotspots and purchase or restore land that can serve as wildlife corridors between the core protected areas. Large corporate donations can fund the purchase and management of land in biodiversity hotspots and move us closer to the *Half-Earth* goal.

Of course, not all companies and industries have identified biodiversity conservation as a primary concern based on the impact of their operations. Companies typically direct charitable giving towards issues that they perceive are related to their core business. For example, it would seem rather strange for a health-care organization to focus its charitable contributions on the conservation of rhinos. Instead, health-care organizations typically donate money to charitable causes that are related to human health, such as funding efforts to fight cancer, combat heart disease, and decrease obesity rates. Environmental issues like biodiversity and wildlife conservation are not perceived to be closely aligned with their core mission. Thankfully, a surprising variety of companies and industries do see a link between a healthy planet and a healthy business, and many companies make charitable contributions to support biodiversity and wildlife conservation efforts throughout the world.

Charitable giving is a popular strategy in the world of business since it is effective and easy to do. However, like Strategy #1, companies may be missing some low-hanging fruit in the form of cost savings and revenues if they choose to implement a tithing strategy as a standalone approach to corporate environmental management.

Strategy #3: Reduction of Costs by Reduction of Environmental Impacts

This is a popular strategy, for good reason, among business of all sizes and shapes. This approach often produces win-win outcomes that are good for the environment and good for business, typically in the form of pollution prevention, waste minimization, energy efficiency, water-use efficiency, and green-building initiatives.

With this strategy, a company identifies cost-saving opportunities that are also good for the environment. Some companies start with a goal to identify cost-saving opportunities and stumble upon the associated environmental benefits after the fact. Other companies deliberately use an environmental lens to view all aspects of the company's inputs and outputs to identify opportunities to reduce, reuse, and recycle. Common goals include reducing the use of paper, improving energy and fleet efficiency, substituting hazardous materials with better alternatives, improving water-use efficiency, and reducing waste.

Some companies take this strategy a step further through the adoption of Design for the Environment (DfE) initiatives. DfE is a design approach—often with the aid of software tools—with the goal of reducing the overall life-cycle environmental impacts of a product, process, or service by assessing raw materials, packaging, solid and hazardous waste, energy and water use, and other relevant factors.

Viewing your company through an environmental lens can be an excellent way to identify incremental improvements that are good for the bottom line and the environment. The analyses can be complex, but they often yield some fantastic opportunities to cut costs, generate revenue, and reduce your company's environmental impacts.

■ Strategy #4: Management of Environmental Risk

For many business managers, environmental management is synonymous with risk management, particularly for companies in industries that attract a significant amount of attention from consumer groups, nonprofit organizations, and regulatory agencies. With this strategy, the primary objective is to avoid costs that are associated with an industrial accident, an environmental lawsuit, or a consumer boycott by using proactive methods that demonstrate a genuine effort to minimize environmental impacts. Taken further, a company can derive a competitive advantage in its industry through the effective management of business risks associated with environmental problems, which we will discuss further in Strategy #6.

A variety of processes and tools can be used to identify and prioritize environmental risks. Regardless of the method you choose, the list of factors typically includes economic, legal, social, political, and technological considerations.

However, it's not always easy to demonstrate the return on environmental-risk investments or to accurately assess what level of investment is best for your business.

There's also a perception that it's easy to overspend on environmental risk-reduction initiatives. As a result, environmental risk-management initiatives are often the first items on the chopping block when a company faces cost-cutting pressures. To prepare for this situation, managers who are responsible for developing and implementing environmental-risk initiatives should be ready to clearly articulate why they believe that the level and type of investments they selected are appropriate for the business.

Despite the challenges of implementing a sound environmental risk-management program, it's a popular strategy, which is a good indicator that many companies consider it a wise investment for their business.

■ Strategy #5: Differentiation of Environmental Products

The idea behind this strategy is that companies can improve revenues, or their position in the industry, by creating products and processes that offer greater environmental benefits or impose greater environmental costs on competitors. Ideally, the new product or process will immediately save money for the company by lowering the cost of raw materials, lowering disposal costs, or creating markets for waste products generated from the company's operations; however, this is not always the case. The new investment will often cost the business more money in the short term, with the expectation of greater profits in the long term by enabling the company to raise prices and capture additional market share.

For the product-differentiation strategy to work, the following three conditions must apply for your company:

1. Customers are willing to pay more for your environmentally friendly product or process;
2. Your company is viewed as credible when it communicates the environmental benefits of your products or processes. If this isn't the case, then your company is at risk of being tagged with the label of "greenwashing" (i.e., when consumers believe that your company spends more time claiming to be green than implementing business practices that minimize environmental impacts); and

3. Your company can protect itself from competitors that imitate your products or processes long enough to generate a positive return on your investment.

If any of these three conditions break down, then a product-differentiation strategy won't work for your business; however, if the three conditions apply to your business, then Strategy #5 is an excellent option to consider.

Strategy #6: A Difficult Life for Your Competitors

At first glance, this strategy may sound like Strategy #5, but the two strategies are fundamentally different and can be uncovered by asking the question, "Am I better off if my competitors match my investment or if they don't match my investment?" If the latter situation applies, you're looking at a product-differentiation strategy (Strategy #5); if the former applies, you're in Strategy #6 territory.

With this strategy, companies use environmental issues to improve their position relative to competitors since it will require more time and resources for competitors to implement the measures relative to your own effort. A well-known example is the 1985 Responsible Care initiative, which was created by several large companies in the chemical industry. Each of the founding companies could implement the voluntary standards, so there wasn't a product-differentiation benefit. However, smaller competitors were not able to easily imitate their larger counterparts without incurring a greater cost, relatively speaking. This gave the Responsible Care companies a competitive advantage over their competition.

Strategy #6 generally comes in two flavors:

1. Voluntary standards that will be beneficial to your business relative to some of your competitors; and
2. Encouraging regulatory agencies to create regulations that are more favorable to your products or processes or tie up your competitors with government regulators.

For Strategy #6 to work, several conditions must be true:

- You need to have measurable performance standards;
- Voluntary programs need to be compatible with other regulations, such as antitrust laws;

- Regulators must have access to information to verify compliance and enforce the standards; and
- Private regulations must apply to all relevant competitors.

Raising the game for your competitors can be an effective strategy that has the potential to improve your business while reducing environmental impacts of your business and industry.

Strategy #7: Redefinition of Your Market

Our last strategy is the most difficult to implement, but it has the potential to yield massive benefits for your company and the environment. With this strategy, you attempt to redefine your market with a solution that benefits the environment. For example, Tesla Motors was launched with the mission "to accelerate the world's transition to sustainable energy."[2] Tesla is seeking to change the industry by proving that electric cars can be better than gasoline-powered cars. That's the type of game-changing strategy to which this strategy refers.

These game-changing strategies don't always work out well. Monsanto tried to redefine the agriculture industry by moving away from traditional insecticides for insect pests and transferring genetic material in such a way that the plants themselves would become inedible to crop pests. This was thought to be a highly profitable and environmentally beneficial strategy since it would enable the company to avoid the financial costs and environmental impacts associated with the creation, transport, and application of insecticides. Monsanto was surprised when it faced widespread consumer protests, particularly in Europe, over the sale of genetically modified food that was given the nickname "Frankenfood."[3]

Breakthrough strategies that redefine your market aren't easy to implement, but the rewards can be huge. Companies like Unilever ("To make sustainable living commonplace"),[4] Chipotle ("Food with Integrity"),[5] Patagonia ("Build the best product, cause no unnecessary harm, use business to inspire and implement solutions to the environmental crisis"),[6] and many others have placed sustainability at the core of their business with great success. Based on survey data, environmentally progressive companies are also better able to attract and retain managers, scientists, and engineers who will enable them to build on their initial success.[7] Never underestimate the ripple effects of creating an organization that is truly committed to sustainability and environmental management.

Conclusion

This chapter outlined seven basic strategies from which to choose when it comes to managing environmental issues for your business. Business managers generally approach environmental problems as business issues and make environmental investments because they expect them to deliver positive returns or reduce risks. As a result, I presented the seven strategies in a way that focuses on the business perspective rather than the environmental benefits.

I recognize that this approach may turn off many readers, particularly those who (like me) are genuinely committed to corporate sustainability and who recognize the inherent value and importance of biodiversity and wildlife conservation. Rest assured that we'll soon look at the conservation-biology side of the equation. Regardless, I hope this chapter gives you a better understanding of how businesses approach environmental issues.

If you work in a corporation, I also hope that this section gives you ideas about which strategy or strategies might be a good fit for your business as well as some perspective on how environmental issues can be leveraged to yield significant benefits for your business and the environment. When business strategies and natural-resource conservation strategies are aligned, they can yield amazing results for corporations, the economy, and the state of the environment.

Chapter 1 Action Steps

1. Reflect on the following questions from the perspective of your organization:
    a. What environmental strategy or combination of strategies has your organization adopted for managing environmental issues?
    b. With what strategy would you like to experiment in your organization?
    c. What can you do to redefine your market and create a healthier planet in the process?
2. Based on the answers to the questions above, what are your next steps to share and implement your ideas?

Chapter 1 Endnotes

1. Edward O. Wilson, *Half-Earth: Our Planet's Fight for Life* (New York: Liveright, 2017), 186.
2. "About Tesla | Tesla." Tesla, Inc. Accessed June 3, 2018. https://www.tesla.com/about.
3. Agence France-Presse, "Tens of thousands march worldwide against Monsanto and GM crops." *The Guardian*. May 23, 2015. Accessed June 3, 2018. https://www.theguardian.com/environment/2015/may/24/tens-of-thousands-march-worldwide-against-monsanto-and-gm-crops.
4. Unilever Global Company, "Our Vision." Accessed June 3, 2018. https://www.unilever.com/about/who-we-are/our-vision.
5. Chipotle, "Food with Integrity." Accessed June 3, 2018. https://www.chipotle.com/food-with-integrity.
6. The Cleanest Line, "Patagonia's Mission Statement." Accessed June 3, 2018. http://www.patagonia.com/company-info.html.
7. Daniel C. Esty and P. J. Simmons, *The Green to Gold Business Playbook: How to Implement Sustainability Practices for Bottom-Line Results in Every Business Function* (Hoboken: John Wiley & Sons, 2011), 12–13.

CHAPTER 2

A Primer on Biodiversity from a Conservation-Biology Perspective

"Destroying rainforest for economic gain is like burning a Renaissance painting to cook a meal."
—E. O. Wilson

The Basics of Biodiversity

Now that we have a better understanding of the corporate perspective on conservation, let's put on a conservation-biology hat to better understand the biologist's perspective on biodiversity and natural-resource conservation. However, before we dive into the details, let's define a few key terms to make sure that we're all on the same page.

The term "biodiversity" is short for "biological diversity," and it refers to the variety of life on Earth. Biodiversity can be described at the gene, species, population, and ecosystem levels. While each of these levels is important to consider, the most common unit of measurement for biodiversity is the species.

A "species" is defined as a group of organisms with a distinctive set of characteristics, such as physical appearance, genetic structure, and behavior, which can be used to distinguish them from other organisms. Some species look radically different from each other; other species look and behave in such similar ways that we must analyze their genetic composition to distinguish them.

The traditional definition of "species" also mentions that members of the same species, under natural conditions, can mate and produce fertile offspring. However, this definition gets confusing when we consider some of the bizarre reproductive strategies that exist in the natural world. For example, certain species of hydra, worms, reptiles, plants, archaea, fungi, bacteria, and insects are capable of asexual reproduction (i.e., where an individual can produce a nearly exact copy of itself without genetic input from another individual). These species can also mate and produce fertile offspring; they just choose not to use this approach under certain conditions.

Regardless of our definition of "species," it's safe to say that there are a lot of them. So far, we've identified over two million species on Earth, a number that is conservatively estimated to represent about 20% of all species on our planet.[1] That number may turn out to be wildly inaccurate once we learn more about the microbial world. When we consider that there are more than 600 species of bacteria living in our mouth,[2] and an estimated four million bacterial species living in a ton of fertile soil,[3] we could be way off base in our estimates. Nobody knows how many microbial species exist, and guesses range from 10 million to one billion species. As the saying goes, when it comes to biodiversity, the Earth is a little-known planet. At the rate we're going, it's estimated that we won't complete the global census of biodiversity until we're well into the 23rd century.

Identifying species is just the beginning. Each species plays a specific role in its habitat, and there are many species interdependencies in any given ecosystem. Given that we don't even know 80% of the species on the planet, it's safe to say that we're still in our infancy when it comes to understanding and mapping the complex species interactions that make up healthy, functioning ecosystems. This is a key reason why many conservationists prefer to protect large chunks of land as preserves rather than tinker with ecosystem dynamics that we don't fully understand. Other biologists disagree, believing that we can analyze the interactions of a subset of key indicator species and use that data to guide our natural resource-management decisions.

The complex study of ecosystems and species interdependencies will be a hot field within conservation biology in the decades to come. Eventually, the field will mature to a point where we'll be able to accurately predict, in excruciating detail, what will happen if we introduce new species or remove species from a specific habitat; however, it looks like it will take a long time before we get there.

While there may be some disagreement on the best way to assess and manage ecosystem health today, when it comes to identifying the biggest threats to biodiversity on this planet, most biologists agree. Biologists use the acronym HIPPO to list, in order, the biggest threats to biodiversity: habitat destruction, invasive species, pollution, human overpopulation, and overharvesting. Climate change is part of "H" as it plays a major role in altering and destroying habitats.

The impact that most corporations have on biodiversity is concentrated in the areas of habitat destruction and pollution, although some companies also play a significant role in the issues of invasive species and overharvesting.

As for human overpopulation, I don't see many companies touching that hot potato anytime soon, so I won't have much to say on that topic in this book. Thankfully, many experts believe that the population-growth issue will work itself out over the coming century as the population growth rate is falling and will likely continue to fall, leading to an end of population growth towards the end of this century.[4]

However, there are two important caveats to that statistic:

1. Per-capita consumption is expected to increase in many parts of the world, although this does not necessarily translate into a larger ecological footprint.[5]
2. Sub-Saharan Africa is expected to witness large population increases that pose a major threat to wildlife and protected areas on the continent and may lead to large increases in the number of African refugees fleeing degraded land and moving to more hospitable parts of the world.[6]

Population growth is no doubt a major issue for wildlife and biodiversity conservation, but it's not an issue that private corporations are expected to address.

Current State / Trends in Biodiversity

As mentioned earlier in this chapter, we've currently identified and named over two million species, and we have a long way to go before we can expect a full catalog of all species on Earth. Here's an approximate breakdown of the number of known species (as of 2016) compared with the anticipated final tally of species that we expect to identify at some point in the future.

	# of Known Species	**# of Species Awaiting Discovery**
Mammals	6,495	~25 new species per year
Birds	~10,000	2 to 3 new species per year
Reptiles	~9,000	1,000
Fishes	~32,000	10,000
Amphibians	~6,600	8,400
Flowering plants	~270,000	80,000
The rest of the living world (e.g., invertebrates, algae, fungi, and gymnosperms)	1.7 million	5 to 100 million

Source: All data from Edward O. Wilson, *Half-Earth: Our Planet's Fight for Life* (New York: Liveright, 2017), 17-18; however, the number of known species of mammals (6,495) and estimated number awaiting discover (25 per year) is from the Oxford University Press USA. "There are more mammal species than we thought." ScienceDaily. Accessed June 3, 2018. www.sciencedaily.com/releases/2018/02/180206090658.htm.

Most species are found in the so-called "biodiversity hotspots" of the world, such as the Amazon region, the Congo Basin, and New Guinea. The 35 areas around the world that qualify as biodiversity hotspots represent just 2.3% of Earth's land surface, but they support more than half of the world's plant species as endemics (species that are only found nowhere else) and nearly 43% of bird, mammal, reptile, and amphibian species as endemics.[7]

Let's not forget our oceans. Oceans cover 71% of the planet's surface and make up more than 95% of the biosphere, but an estimated 91% of species in the ocean have yet to be discovered, described, and catalogued, partly because less than 5% of the oceans have been explored.[8] Oceans are an extremely rich, and largely unexplored, resource.

As of 2015, every sovereign nation in the world has some form of protected-area system in place to protect native species. This includes roughly 161,000 reserves on land and 6,500 reserves over marine waters, representing roughly 15% of the Earth's land area and 2.8% of the Earth's ocean area,[9] although these figures vary depending on how we define "protected area." No matter what estimate you use, when we consider Wilson's *Half-Earth* goal discussed in Chapter 1, we clearly have a long way to go. We don't have enough land set aside to provide sufficient protection for global biodiversity, but the good news is that the protected-area coverage trend is moving in the right direction and gradually increasing.

Unfortunately, the trend for extinction rates is headed in the wrong direction. Extinction rates are estimated to be 100 to 1,000 times higher now than what occurred in the days before humans.[10] The actual number depends on how many species exist, which, as we've already seen, is a number with a significant amount of uncertainty. Regardless, there's a consensus among scientists that the current rate of species extinction is well beyond anything that we've seen in human history.[11]

Some experts believe that 30% to 50% of all species will be gone within the next century.[12] This projection is despite significant global-conservation efforts that have lowered the overall extinction rate by an estimated 20%.[13] Over the past 500 years, approximately 850 species have been listed as extinct by the International Union for Conservation of Nature (IUCN), and many more species will likely disappear before we have a chance to discover and learn about them. At present, the IUCN lists more than 91,250 species on its IUCN Red List of Threatened Species, and more than 25,820 of these species are threatened with extinction, including 41% of amphibians, 34% of conifers, 33% of reef-building corals, 25% of mammals, and 13% of birds.[14]

This extinction threat is not limited to species in the rainforests of the Amazon or New Guinea. We're facing plenty of biodiversity challenges in our own backyard. Scientists at NatureServe estimate that about one-third of all U.S. species (~8,500 species) are at risk of extinction.[15] The North American Bird Conservation Initiatives has placed 432 of the 1,154 avian species of the United States on a Watch List of species that are "most at risk of extinction without significant action."[16]

The Value Proposition for Business

Whenever the topic of business and biodiversity comes up, it's common for someone in the audience to ask, "Why should companies care about protecting biodiversity?" Why should a company care if some obscure worm, fish, insect, or microscopic soil dweller goes extinct? The link between business and biodiversity is not always obvious. There are a variety of answers to the all-important, value-proposition question, and they generally fall into three buckets: ecosystem services, ethics and religion, and profitable conservation.

Ecosystem Services

The most popular answer to the value-proposition question relates to the concept of "ecosystem services"—the processes through which natural ecosystems and their constituent species sustain and fulfill human life. Each of us benefits from ecosystem services that are often taken for granted, such as the pollination of crops and natural vegetation, the purification of water and air, climate regulation, flood and pest control, soil retention, and detoxification and decomposition of waste. Estimates vary widely, but studies calculate that the Earth's biosphere provides anywhere from US$ 16 to US$ 125 trillion worth of services per year, free of charge, for the good of people, businesses, and the planet.[17] It logically follows that, since businesses share in the benefits derived from ecosystem services, they also share responsibility for protecting the ecosystems and species that provide these services.

Let's look at some of these ecosystem services in more detail to get a better understanding of what we're talking about. Here are five of the more prominent categories of ecosystem services that benefit human society: provisioning of products, regulating / stabilizing the environment, supporting services, biomedical research and infectious-disease prevention, and cultural services.

Provisioning of Products

Ecosystems provide an abundance of food, fiber, wood, and other resources that humans use for nourishment, shelter, and fuel. For example, fish from our oceans serve as a protein source for more than three billion people worldwide, generating an estimated export value of more than US$ 150 billion each year.[18]

Nature also provides a long list of medicines that are used to treat and cure diseases. More than half of the most-prescribed medicines come from natural sources, either directly from the source or indirectly in the form of a template that we use to create new drugs.[19] In the developing world, the World Health Organization estimates that as many as 80% of residents rely on medicines derived from natural sources.[20] Given that worldwide pharmaceutical revenues have reached over US$ 1 trillion,[21] society and businesses are getting some massive economic and health benefits from naturally sourced medicines. These figures are particularly impressive when we consider that less than 1% of all known plant species have been analyzed for their potential use in medicine.[22] We may just be scratching the surface when it comes to uncovering the health and economic benefits that nature can provide.

Regulating / Stabilizing the Environment

While we work, play, and sleep, plants and soil microbes are busy purifying water, cleaning air, controlling erosion, mitigating floods, storing carbon, detoxifying soils, and controlling pests and disease-causing pathogens. Insect species, such as the praying mantis, provide free extermination services that control over half of the insect species that we call "pests."

The value of these ecosystem services does not always go unnoticed. In what is considered a poster-child project for ecosystem services, New York City made the unusual decision to attempt to purify the city's drinking water by protecting its watershed rather than building a filtration plant. Instead of spending US$ 8 to US$ 10 billion (in today's dollars) to build and maintain a filtration plant, the city spent US$ 1.5 billion in 1997 to purchase thousands of acres of land in upstate New York, improve treatment plants and septic systems, shield its reservoirs from pollution, and subsidize environmentally sound economic development that protects the watershed.[23] This initiative is still widely hailed as a success to this day.

Supporting Services

"Supporting services" refers to ecosystem services such as primary production (where plants make their own food), nutrient cycling, and pollination, which serve as a foundation for all other ecosystem services. Plants use photosynthesis to create the energy base that fuels all ecological processes. Global nutrient cycles move nutrients through the environment, so they can be used by organisms in processes such as the decay of organic materials. Insects, animals, and plants work together to transport pollen and seeds, which enables plants to reproduce and move to new locations. These ecosystem services provide significant economic value to businesses and society.

Let's look at the economic value of bee pollination as an example. Honey bees contribute more than US$ 15 billion to the U.S. economy through their role as pollinators of commercial crops.[24] At a more micro level, a study of coffee farms in Central America found that, by preserving forested areas around coffee farms, crop yields improved, and average incomes increased by US$ 62,000 per year, representing 7% of the annual income of a typical farm.[25] This success has been attributed to the pollination services provided by bees in the adjacent forest. The coffee-plant flowers located near the forest received twice as many bee visits and pollen transfers, resulting in a 20% greater yield in coffee beans when compared with coffee plants located further away from the forest.[26]

Biomedical Research and Infectious-Disease Prevention

The many species living in a healthy ecosystem function as living laboratories and contain a treasure trove of genetic material, anatomical features, and physiological characteristics, which have been priceless in helping us understand human health and disease. The benefits of medical research are in the trillions of dollars per year, and a significant chunk of that benefit can be attributed to the living laboratory of animals and plants in nature.[27]

Cultural Services

While more difficult to measure, we also obtain many benefits from healthy ecosystems in the form of aesthetic beauty, intellectual stimulation, spiritual development, outdoor recreation, and a sense of place. Some of these services can be quantified, such as the value derived from ecotourism or the real-estate value of homes and businesses located near pristine natural areas. Protected areas receive an estimated eight billion visits per year, which generate an estimated US$ 600 billion per year in direct spending globally.[28] That's a healthy sum compared to the estimated US$ 10 billion spent annually on safeguarding and managing these protected areas.[29] Even if we triple or quadruple our estimate of the amount of money needed to adequately safeguard existing natural areas, that's still a hefty profit from an ecosystem-services perspective.

Other services, such as the emotional, spiritual, and intellectual values derived from spending time in biodiverse natural settings, are more difficult to assess but are nonetheless clearly important to human society. Just ask the countless artists, poets, writers, musicians, architects, and others who have created celebrated works inspired by nature.

The Value Proposition of Biodiversity Revisited

Before we leave the topic of ecosystem services, I'd like to add two more important points that speak directly to the role that biodiversity plays in ecosystem health.

First, it's important to recognize that biodiversity plays a critical role in healthy, functioning ecosystems by increasing ecosystem stability and productivity. This can be measured in a variety of ways, such as the amount of biomass grown, nutrient availability, and atmospheric carbon that is photosynthesized into carbohydrate. Many studies suggest that more biodiverse ecosystems are more productive, healthy ecosystems.

Second, it's important to understand that, when we remove even one species from a healthy, functioning ecosystem, it can have far-reaching consequences. Among the many examples from which to draw, let's look at the well-known example of sea otters in California.

When sea otters were hunted for their pelts along the California coast, it had a major, negative impact on the kelp beds of the coastal ecosystem.[30] This was because sea otters eat sea urchins, and sea urchins enjoy munching on kelp. Once the sea-otter population declined due to hunting, the population of sea urchins increased substantially, and the now-abundant sea urchins depleted the kelp beds. After a sea-otter hunting ban was implemented, the original health of the coastal ecosystem returned.[31]

The lesson learned from this and from many other examples is that, when we remove species from an ecosystem, we also remove numerous species interactions that we often don't fully understand until after the fact. Like a game of Jenga, we often can't tell in advance if the removal of one species from an ecosystem will cause the entire structure to come crashing down.

We've only scratched the surface on the topic of ecosystem services. An entire book can be written on this topic and, in fact, many already have. However, I hope this summary gives you an appreciation of the value that ecosystem services provide to human society and the role that biodiversity plays in maintaining healthy ecosystems.

Ethics and Religion

Another common response to the question of why businesses should be interested in biodiversity conservation is that it's simply the right thing to do, regardless of the benefits that wildlife and biodiversity provide to human health and society. This sentiment may be framed from an ethical, a religious, or a responsible corporate-citizen perspective.

Ethics

In this context, "ethics" refers to the moral principles that govern an organization's behavior. Here's an important question: "Is it moral to directly or indirectly contribute to the loss of biodiversity and wildlife without taking steps to mitigate or minimize the problem?" Some will argue, "Yes," some will argue, "No," and some will say, "It depends. The "It depends" group may provide examples of species that they would like to see disappear, like mosquitoes or the Guinea worm.

Even many animal lovers and conservation biologists may reluctantly agree that the extinction of the Guinea worm would be a good thing. It's not a very lovable creature. The worm's larvae hang out in ponds and other stagnant water where they are eaten by tiny "water fleas." People then drink the flea-inhabited water.

Once the fleas are in our stomach, the Guinea worm larvae are released from the water fleas, penetrate our digestive tract, and enter our body cavity. Over the next 10 to 14 months, the female larvae grow into adult worms, which are 2 to 3 feet long and resemble spaghetti noodles. Around that time, the worms decide that it's time to get out of our body. To do this, they create a blister on our skin, usually on our legs or feet. This blister is extremely painful and makes our skin feel like it's burning. Our logical response is to attempt to relieve the burning pain by immersing our body part in water. Once immersed in water, the Guinea worm leaves the human through the wound and releases millions of immature larvae back into the water, and the cycle repeats.

There is no vaccine to prevent infection and no drug to treat the Guinea worm. The worm can be surgically removed by a doctor in a medical facility, but that option is often unavailable in the remote parts of Africa where the worm is still found. Instead, the customary practice is to coax part of the worm out of the wound, and then pull it out a few centimeters each day by winding it around a small stick or a piece of gauze. This painful process may take weeks to complete and can cause secondary bacterial infections that make the pain even worse. A person may be unable to function for weeks or months, and permanent damage can occur if their joints get infected and become locked. Yes, it's easy to see why many people would like to see that critter disappear from the face of the Earth!

A good friend of mine is a conservation biologist, and he spent several years working for a nonprofit organization in South Sudan with the goal of eliminating the Guinea worm. His organization focused on preventive efforts, such as teaching people to avoid drinking unsafe water, encouraging people to use a cloth or pipe filter to remove the water fleas from the water before drinking, and preventing individuals with swelling or wounds from entering ponds and other drinking-water sources. These efforts appear to be working, as the number of cases of Guinea worm has decreased from 3.5 million per year in 1986 to just 126 cases in 2014.[32] Only four countries now have local cases: Chad, Ethiopia, Mali, and South Sudan.

That's a long and gross example, but it does give us something to ponder in our answer to the ethical question of whether all forms of life should be protected—even for species like the Guinea worm, which cause great harm to humans. Thankfully, only about 1,000 known species (out of the two million known species and 10 million estimated species) are sufficiently detrimental to human life[33] to perhaps justify the eradication of these species from a human perspective. Of course, we would also want to understand and consider the trade-offs from an ecosystem-health perspective given the ripple effect that may result from the removal of a species.

Species like the Guinea worm and disease-carrying mosquitoes provide some interesting food for thought when answering the question, "Is all life worth protecting?"

Religion

Let's ponder another interesting question: "Is all life sacred?"

Religion has the potential to play an important role in biodiversity and natural-resource conservation. Several religious leaders have spoken out on the ethical and scriptural mandate to protect natural resources. Let's look at two of the more vocal religious leaders on the topic of biodiversity and natural-resource conservation: Pope Francis and the 14th Dalai Lama.

The Catholic Church has a relatively long history of speaking out, albeit quietly, on the importance of protecting the environment, starting with Saint Francis of Assisi (1181/1182–1226), the patron saint of animals and ecology. This Catholic mystic is well known for his preaching and songs to the sun and moon, the flowers and birds, and all other creatures on Earth, and for expressing love and concern for animals and nature as well as the poor and outcast.

In 1971, we started to hear popes express concern about the state of the environment when Pope Paul VI said, "Due to an ill-considered exploitation of nature, humanity runs the risk of destroying it and becoming in turn a victim of this degradation."[34]

Then, in 1991, Pope John Paul II expanded on this call for a global ecological conversion, along with the need to "safeguard the moral conditions for an authentic human ecology."[35] He stressed that authentic human development has a moral character that presumes full respect for both the human person and our connection to the world around us.

Since that time, popes have become increasingly outspoken about the need for environmental protection. In 2012, Pope Benedict XVI, whom some called "The Green Pope," frequently spoke and wrote about the environment, climate change, and other conservation topics. He proposed "eliminating the structural causes of the dysfunctions of the world economy and correcting models of growth which have proved incapable of ensuring respect for the environment."[36] Like Pope John Paul II, Pope Benedict XVI emphasized that "the deterioration of nature is closely connected to the culture which shapes human coexistence,"[37] pointing out the damage that's being done to both the natural environment and our social environment. Pope Benedict XVI's writings and teachings on the topic of the environment were eventually collected into a book simply titled, *The Environment.*

In July 2015, Pope Francis continued to ramp up the topic of the environment with the publication of his book, *Laudato Si: On Care for Our Common Home.* In *Laudato Si*, Pope Francis summarizes what he terms "the present ecological crisis,"[38] touching on the topics of pollution, climate change, water, biodiversity, global inequality, and the deterioration of society.

Specific to biodiversity, Pope Francis writes the following:

> "Each year sees the disappearance of thousands of plant and animal species which we will never know, which our children will never see, because they have been lost forever. The great majority

> become extinct for reasons related to human activity. Because of us, thousands of species will no longer give glory to God by their very existence, nor convey their message to us. We have no such right."[39]

Pope Francis follows this up with a call to action for all of us to "cooperate as instruments of God for the care of creation, each according to his or her own culture, experience, involvements, and talents."[40]

Even though Catholic Church leadership is becoming more vocal on the need for environmental protection and natural-resource conservation, most Catholic parishes today lack ministries that support conservation efforts in the local community. However, with the recent call to action from Pope Francis, we may find that the Catholic Church, and its 1.2 billion members, may become a significant force in biodiversity and natural-resource conservation. To facilitate this movement, in June 2016, the Vatican marked the first anniversary of Pope Francis's encyclical on the environment with the launch of a new website (www.laudatosi.va), which provides information on how to put Pope Francis's teaching into practice.

For another religious perspective, let's look at the Buddhist approach to the topic of biodiversity and natural-resource conservation. In the world of Buddhism, the 14th Dalai Lama has been a prominent advocate for conservation and the environment, sharing many environmental messages for the 500 million members of the Buddhist faith. Many of the Dalai Lama's statements can be found online (www.dalailama.com/messages/environment).

For starters, Buddhists believe in reincarnation, which carries a built-in concern for the future. After all, if you expect to be reborn, you probably don't want to emerge into a world where the environment is trashed. The Dalai Lama contrasts this way of thinking from Western thought that typically focuses on the practical side of things for the present generation of human beings.

Buddhism also teaches that the ultimate nature is "emptiness," referring to the emptiness of a true or independent existence. This concept is extended to the environment, and Buddhists believe in a close interrelation between the natural environment and the sentient beings living within it. Everything is connected.

Finally, Buddhism teaches the importance of nonviolence—another concept easily applied to nature. The Dalai Lama believes that nonviolence applies to any living thing that has a mind, and we should not harm or destroy anything indiscriminately. Instead, we share a sense of universal responsibility for both mankind and nature.

To wrap up this section on religion, I'll leave you with the following call to action from the Dalai Lama:

> "It is not difficult to forgive destruction in the past which resulted from ignorance. Today however we have access to more information, and it is essential that we re-examine ethically what we have inherited, what we are responsible for, and what we will pass on to coming generations. Many of the Earth's habitats, animals, plants, insects and even micro-organisms that we know as rare may not be known at all by future generations. We have the capability and the responsibility. We must act before it is too late."[41]

Responsible Corporate Citizen

Another variation of the "it's-the-right-thing-to-do" concept is the idea that companies have an obligation to be responsible corporate citizens or responsible neighbors. This is often interpreted with the implication that companies should do more than what is required by law. Companies should operate in ways that do no harm to the environment of the local community—or anywhere else for that matter—regardless of the letter of the law. Corporations should be responsible members of the community, and this includes doing their part to protect local wildlife and biodiversity.

Profitable Conservation

Finally, a third answer to the question of why companies should be interested in biodiversity conservation is the anthropocentric view that it can be profitable. Whether or not we like to think about it this way, most companies are driven primarily by profit and will do little beyond what they feel is required by law and society when it comes to the environment.

Fortunately, this profit motive can be a powerful ally in natural-resource conservation. The quest for profit can be used to motivate companies to take actions that they would otherwise not consider. These actions are good for biodiversity and the environment as well as for business in the form of cutting costs, reducing risk, and generating new revenue streams. This concept, of course, is the main goal of this book: to explore business strategies that are profitable for business, biodiversity, and wildlife.

I certainly don't want to detract from the importance of ethics and religion as it relates to biodiversity and natural-resource conservation. These important perspectives have the potential to mobilize many of us—as individuals—to do our part to protect the environment. However, for many businesses, the best way to align the interests of corporations, biodiversity, and wildlife is to demonstrate how natural-resource conservation can also be profitable. In the pages that follow, we'll focus our attention on the best things that companies can do to protect wildlife and biodiversity while making a profit.

Chapter 2 Action Steps

1. At a personal level, how would you answer the question, "Why should I care about protecting biodiversity and natural resources?"
2. From your company's perspective, how would you answer the question, "Why should our company care about protecting biodiversity and natural resources?"
3. Over which elements of HIPPO does your company have the greatest impact or influence?

Chapter 2 Endnotes

1. Edward O. Wilson, *Half-Earth: Our Planet's Fight for Life* (New York: Liveright, 2017), 21.
2. Society for General Microbiology, "New Bacterial Species Found In Human Mouth." ScienceDaily. August 11, 2008. Accessed June 3, 2018. www.sciencedaily.com/releases/2008/08/080810214006.htm.
3. E. O. Wilson, transcript of "My wish: Build the Encyclopedia of Life." TED: Ideas Worth Spreading. Accessed June 3, 2018. https://www.ted.com/talks/e_o_wilson_on_saving_life_on_earth/transcript.
4. Max Roser and Estaban Ortiz-Ospina, "World Population Growth." Our World in Data. First published in 2013; updated April 2017. Accessed June 3, 2018. https://ourworldindata.org/world-population-growth.

5. Note 1, supra, 191–92.

6. Benjamin Wormald, "Sub-Saharan Africa." Pew Research Center Religion & Public Life Project. April 2, 2015. Accessed June 3, 2018. http://www.pewforum.org/2015/04/02/sub-saharan-africa/.

7. Conservation International, "Why hotspots matter: A history." Accessed June 3, 2018. https://www.conservation.org/How/Pages/Hotspots.aspx.

8. Census of Marine Life, "How many species on Earth? About 8.7 million, new estimate says." ScienceDaily. August 24, 2011. Accessed June 3, 2018. www.sciencedaily.com/releases/2011/08/110823180459.htm; *see also* National Ocean Service (National Oceanic and Atmospheric Administration and the U.S. Department of Commerce). "How much of the ocean have we explored?" January 1, 2009. Accessed June 3, 2018. https://oceanservice.noaa.gov/facts/exploration.html.

9. Note 1, supra, 186.

10. Ibid., 54.

11. Ibid., 54–55.

12. Center for Biological Diversity, "The Endangered Species Act: A Wild Success." Accessed June 4, 2018. http://www.biologicaldiversity.org/campaigns/esa_wild_success.

13. Note 1, supra, 55–56.

14. IUCN, "The IUCN Red List of Threatened Species." May 29, 2018. Accessed June 4, 2018. https://www.iucn.org/theme/species/our-work/iucn-red-list-threatened-species.

15. Paul Tolme, "The U.S. Biodiversity Crisis," National Wildlife, February–March 2017.

16. Ibid.

17. Robert Costanza, Rudolf de Groot, Paul Sutton, Sander van der Ploeg, Sharolyn J. Anderson, Ida Kubiszewski, Stephen Farber, and R. Kerry Turner. 2014, "Changes in the Global Value of Ecosystem Services." Global Environmental Change 26 (May): 152–58.

18. Ocean Assets Institute, "Seafood—Investing in the Blue Economy." Accessed June 4, 2018. https://www.oceanassets.org/seafood.html.

19. Eric Chivian and Aaron Bernstein, *Sustaining Life: How Human Health Depends on Biodiversity* (Oxford: Oxford University Press, 2008), 117.

20. Ibid.

21. John Laporte, "Topic: Global Pharmaceutical Industry." Statista. Accessed June 4, 2018. https://www.statista.com/topics/1764/global-pharmaceutical-industry/.

22. Note 19, supra, 117–118.

23. Alice Kenny, "Ecosystem Services in the New York City Watershed." Forest Trends. January 1, 2001. Accessed June 4, 2018. https://www.forest-trends.org/ecosystem_marketplace/ecosystem-services-in-the-new-york-city-watershed-1969-12-31.

24. Joseph S. Wilson and Olivia Messinger Carril, *The Bees in Your Backyard* (Princeton: Princeton University Press, 2016), 247.

25. T. H. Ricketts, G. C. Daily, P. R. Ehrlich, and C. D. Michener, "Economic Value of Tropical Forest to Coffee Production." Proceedings of the National Academy of Sciences 101, no. 34 (2004): 12579-2582. doi:10.1073/pnas.0405147101.

26. Ibid.

27. Note 19, supra, 163.

28. A. Balmford, J. M. H. Green, M. Anderson, J. Beresford, C. Huang, R. Naidoo, M. Walpole, and A. Manica (2015), "Walk on the Wild Side: Estimating the Global Magnitude of Visits to Protected Areas." PLoS Biol 13(2): e1002074. doi:10.1371/journal.pbio.1002074.

29. Ibid.

30. Associated Press, "Predator sea otter now more of a hero in California coastal ecosystem." The Washington Post. May 18, 2018. Accessed June 4, 2018. https://www.washingtonpost.com/lifestyle/kidspost/predator-sea-otter-now-more-of-a-hero-in-california-coastal-ecosystem/2018/05/18/847269b4-5a15-11e8-858f-12becb4d6067_story.html?noredirect=on&utm_term=.918dee6673ef.

31. Ibid.

32. Centers for Disease Control and Prevention, "Infographic: Guinea Worm." August 4, 2015. Accessed June 4, 2018. https://www.cdc.gov/globalhealth/infographics/guinea_worm.htm.

33. Note 1, supra, 53.

34. Pope Francis, *Laudato Si: On Care for Our Common Home* (Vatican City: Sunday Visitor Publishing Division, 2015), 7.

35. Ibid., 8.

36. Ibid.

37. Ibid.

38. Ibid., 15.

39. Ibid., 26.

40. Ibid., 15.

41. His Holiness the Dalai Lama, "Universal Responsibility and the Environment." Buddha Dharma Education Association & BuddhaNet. Accessed June 04, 2018. https://www.buddhanet.net/e-learning/buddhism/bs-s13a.htm.

PART 2

Profitable-Conservation Strategies for Wildlife and Biodiversity

This part includes five chapters, which cover key profitable-conservation strategies that address four of the five major threats to biodiversity and wildlife: habitat destruction (Chapter 3), invasive species (Chapter 4), pollution (Chapter 5), and overharvesting (Chapter 6). This section does not include the threat of human overpopulation since companies are not expected to address this challenge. Chapter 7 provides an overview of sustainability reporting specific to biodiversity and wildlife conservation.

CHAPTER 3

Habitat Destruction: Profitable-Conservation Strategies

"We are faced not with two separate crises, one environmental and the other social, but rather with one complex crisis, which is both social and environmental. Strategies for a solution demand an integrated approach to combating poverty, restoring dignity to the excluded and at the same time protecting nature."

—Pope Francis

Habitat Destruction

Habitat destruction is the #1 issue that impacts wildlife and biodiversity today.[1] This fact shouldn't come as much of a surprise. When we think of all the roads, power lines, buildings, clearcutting, and other development activities taking place all over the world, we can quickly get a sense of the widespread reality of this issue.

The World Wildlife Fund estimates that forests cover about 31% of the land area on Earth[2] and, for a variety of reasons, we're losing about 46,000 to 58,000 square miles of forest each year—roughly equivalent to losing 48 football fields every minute.[3] In the Amazon alone, we've lost about 17% of the forest over the past 50 years, mostly due to forest conversion for cattle ranching.[4] Habitat destruction is clearly a big issue, and it won't be going away anytime soon.

The term "habitat destruction" can refer to the complete destruction of a habitat or, more commonly, habitat fragmentation, where a large, continuous area of a habitat is divided into two or more fragments. The primary culprit behind habitat loss, degradation, and fragmentation is a change in land use, usually in the form of agriculture, logging, mining, and urban or residential development. From a business perspective, habitats are commonly fragmented by the construction of roads, power lines, and buildings.

Since habitat fragmentation is such an important factor in the loss of biodiversity, we'll start this section with a primer on the topic. Note that climate change and ocean acidification are often viewed as forms of habitat destruction, but we'll cover those topics in the chapter on pollution (Chapter 5) since the actions that corporations take to address pollution are like the actions they take to combat climate change and ocean acidification.

Habitat fragmentation is characterized by three important conditions that it creates: smaller habitat, increased "edge effects," and increased isolation.

Smaller Habitat

When we fragment a piece of land, the remaining habitat will be smaller than the original chunk of land. That may sound obvious, but it's important to call out because smaller habitats typically support a smaller number of species. In other words, fragmentation generally reduces the number of species that can live in the remaining habitat.

This simple concept is derived from a formula that may make your head hurt. It states that, for any habitat, a reduction in area results in a fraction of the species disappearing over time by roughly the fourth root of the area. *Ouch.* Thankfully, for our purposes, we can pretend that we didn't hear that! Scientists did these types of calculations to create the *Half-Earth* conservation goal designed to protect 85% of the species that exist today.[5] Scientists are now busy identifying and mapping the different habitats that should be included as part of the *Half-Earth* conservation project.

Increased "Edge Effects"

The second important characteristic of habitat fragmentation is that it increases the proportion of habitat edges in relation to the total area. In other words, any given point within the fragment of land is, on average, closer to an edge. Why does that matter? Edges matter because they create changes in the species composition for a given chunk of land.

The species-composition changes found at edges are caused by the following conditions:

- **Edges of a forest have microclimatic changes that impact the types of vegetation that can grow there.** These microclimatic changes include more direct sunlight, higher soil temperatures, differences in humidity and depth of humus, and increased wind exposure and snow loads compared with the interior of a forest. The seeds of some plant species are sensitive to drying out with increased sun and wind, leading to significant differences in the types of vegetation found at a forest edge compared with the forest interior. To make matters worse, these species alterations extend into the forest interior. In some tropical rain forests, vegetation changes can be detected as far as nearly 1,500 feet from the edge.[6] In the scenario where we have a small fragment of a natural habitat or a narrow corridor of land, the microclimatic changes associated with the edges can permeate throughout the entire piece of a habitat. The result may be a decrease in the presence of rare and sensitive species, while weedy species and generalist predators may thrive.
- **Edges are suitable for some species but unsuitable for others.** If we build a road through a forest, some plant species will thrive with the extra sunlight, and some bird species will enjoy perches next to these open areas where they can pounce on exposed prey. Other species will actively shy away from these areas of increased sunlight and exposure, moving further into the interior habitat where the characteristics of land remain unchanged. When we push these species into the now-smaller interior habitat, we are likely to see increased competition for limited resources.
- **Edge-tolerant species are often generalist predators and exotic species that outcompete native species and habitat specialists.** Examples of edge-loving species include brown-headed cowbirds, crows, raccoons, and opossums. These species thrive in an edge habitat and act as nest predators and cavity competitors of interior species, which can decrease the populations of forest songbirds,

ground-nesting birds, reptiles, and amphibians in the remaining habitat fragments.

- **Edges become areas with increased noise, light, pollution, human recreation, and roadkill.** The increased noise, light, and human activity may cause some species to move further inland, away from habitat edges. Traffic on adjacent roads can cause pollution in the form of nitrogen deposition, and the increase in noise and light can deter or disorient animals. Roadkill continues to be a significant source of wildlife mortality with several million collisions per year reported worldwide. In one study in Saguaro National Park on the United States–Mexico border, an estimated 30,000 animals were killed by vehicles annually, which included a variety of reptiles, amphibians, birds, and mammals.[7]

Increased Isolation

The third characteristic of habitat fragmentation states that any given fragment is, on average, more isolated from other habitat fragments. When habitats become less connected, we may see a decrease in the movement of species entering and leaving the habitat fragment. This reduction in mobility can lead to increased competition for resources and mates as well as inbreeding, which can cause genetic abnormalities and a decrease in the average fitness of the population.

So far, we've seen that larger habitat patches typically have more species than small ones, and connected patches have more species than isolated ones. However, there's one important caveat to consider: While retaining larger fragments may help some species survive, if we're left with only one large fragment of land, it increases the risk that a catastrophic event, such as a storm or disease outbreak, will wipe out the remaining individuals in the single-habitat patch.

This scenario occurred with the Panamanian golden frog (*Atelopus zeteki*), a frog species that lives along mountain streams of the mountainous cloud forests of Panama. This brightly colored frog is gold or yellow-green, and some individuals have prominent black spots along their back and legs. While Panamanian golden frogs can make sounds, they also have an endearing communication behavior of waving their arm as if to say, "Hello!" This form of communication is believed to have evolved because of the noise of fast-moving streams where it lives.

Unfortunately, the last known populations of the Panamanian golden frog were rapidly dwindling due to a fungal disease called chytridiomycosis and the loss of critical habitats to farming, livestock, and development. In 2004, the swift spread of chytridiomycosis among the remaining wild populations of the frog led biologists to take the drastic action of removing all known remaining Panamanian golden frogs from the wild and placing them in captive breeding programs across Panama and North America.[8] Panamanian golden frogs are now believed to be extinct in the wild, but the goal is to release captive bred frogs back into the wild at some point in the future.

These types of scenarios make it necessary for scientists to evaluate the pros and cons of establishing one large habitat versus several small habitats. This trade-off has been referred to as the SLOSS debate, where SLOSS is short for "single large or several small" habitats. There's no one answer to the SLOSS question since each species will respond differently to the size, number, and location of habitat patches. However, if you're looking for a general rule of thumb to guide your decisions, go with this advice: Set aside as many reserves as possible, and make these reserves as large as possible.

You may be asking yourself this question: "Don't we already have large reserves of land in the form of national parks and other protected areas?"

The answer: "Yes and no."

We do have a good network of national parks, state parks, and wildlife refuges. The problem is that most parks are too small to conserve some of the resident species. Even the largest national park in the continental United States—Yellowstone National Park—is too small to support viable populations of large carnivores for the long term. In addition, many U.S. national parks are facetiously referred to as "rock and ice" by some conservationists because of their location in deserts and high mountains and their emphasis on conserving landscape views and unique geological features.

Over 90% of all federally threatened and endangered plants and wildlife have some, or all, of their habitat on nonfederal land, and 37% are completely dependent on nonfederal lands.[9] Private landowners, including corporations, clearly have an important role in the effort to protect biodiversity and wildlife populations.

There's a lot more to this discussion, but hopefully this introduction will give you an appreciation for how habitat fragmentation impacts species diversity.

Profitable-Conservation Strategies to Address Habitat Destruction

Now that we have a better understanding of habitat destruction and habitat fragmentation, let's look at four common strategies that corporations use to combat the issue: avoidance, minimization, rehabilitation and restoration, and biodiversity offsets and voluntary compensatory actions. There's also a fifth major strategy— supply chain management—which we'll cover in Chapter 6's discussion of overharvesting.

■ Strategy #1: Avoidance

The first—and best—strategy that companies can adopt to address habitat destruction and biodiversity loss is a simple one: Avoid any development or operations in areas with a high-quality habitat for species that are classified as endangered, threatened, or vulnerable to extinction. This avoidance strategy may also be extended to a high-quality habitat for species that are classified as "species of concern," depending on the health of the populations of those species as well as the degree and types of potential impacts.

An "avoidance" strategy means that we leave the land alone. In practice, the company will also need to monitor and maintain the integrity of the habitat or sell or donate the land to an organization that will do the monitoring and maintenance. To identify these "avoidance zones," you'll need to conduct a biodiversity assessment to collect data about the species that are in the areas where you hope to develop or operate.

Biodiversity assessments consist of three basic steps:

1. **Search relevant, available databases to create a list of species that you'll likely find at each of your sites.** These databases may include Biodiversity Information Serving Our Nation, which is more commonly known by its acronym BISON, and NatureServe. You'll also want to identify the species that are considered endangered, threatened, vulnerable, or species of concern.

2. **Conduct field surveys to identify and confirm species that are found on-site.** The field-survey team will also note observations about habitat condition and disturbances as well as relevant observations about species biology and behavior, such as the location of nesting and foraging sites. Field surveys usually focus on identifying species of plants, mammals, birds, amphibians, and reptiles, along with some invertebrates including butterflies, dragonflies, grasshoppers, bees, beetles, ants, and land crabs. Species that are endangered, threatened, vulnerable, or species of concern are of interest. In other words, these are not intended to be exhaustive inventories that identify all the species in a given area; instead, the field survey focuses on identifying key species and habitat conditions that will help identify areas that should be off limits to development and operations. These field surveys take about five to seven days per site to complete, although large, remote, biodiversity-rich areas can take significantly longer.
3. **Draft a final report, which includes a species inventory and supporting maps.** It can take one to two months to go through the various stages of writing, editing, and approval for the final report.

Keep in mind that an avoidance strategy is not free. There may be significant costs to the company in the form of foregone revenue as well as the cost to identify, monitor, and maintain a habitat in and around the avoidance zones. Despite these costs, many companies find this strategy to be profitable after factoring potential regulatory costs, the risk of protests and lawsuits, and the impact of negative customer and consumer responses to the development of a habitat.

Avoidance was an important strategy that we adopted at the White Sands Missile Range in New Mexico, where I worked as a conservation biologist employee of The Nature Conservancy. "Missile Range" and "Nature Conservancy" may sound like strange bedfellows, but the U.S. Department of Defense hired The Nature Conservancy to help protect and manage the wide variety of ecosystems found on-site.

The White Sands Missile Range has a lot to offer from a biodiversity perspective—more than you might expect given the name. The range contains over 2 million acres (roughly 3,200 square miles) of land, which includes Chihuahuan Desert, grasslands, wetlands, pinyon-juniper woodlands, and a small stand of ponderosa pine in mountains that reach nearly 9,000 feet in elevation. As you might expect, this wide variety of ecosystems yields a rich diversity of plant and animal species, including several threatened and endangered species as well as roughly 4,000 oryx (*Oryx gazella*) from southern Africa.[10]

African oryx (also known as "gemsbok") are large (220 to 530 pounds) species of antelope with long, straight horns that average 33 inches in length, and impressive black-and-white markings on their face and legs. In the 1960s, the New Mexico Department of Game & Fish thought it would be a good idea to establish a population of oryx for public hunting at the White Sands Missile Range. The original herd of roughly 100 animals was expected to increase to several hundred animals; however, despite the active hunting program, the number of oryx on the range skyrocketed to more than 4,000 animals several decades later.[11] Oryx collisions were always a concern while we drove the remote roads of the range, particularly at night.

To implement an avoidance strategy at the White Sands Missile Range, biologists and archeologists conducted field surveys and created maps, which identified areas that should be protected from missile testing and military-training activities due to the presence of certain species, ecosystems, or archaeological sites. For example, several springs and creeks are home to three of the four remaining populations of White Sands pupfish (*Cyprinodon tularosa*), a small (roughly 2 inches long) fish that is listed as a threatened species. The White Sands pupfish is the only species of fish that managed to survive the hydrologic and climatic changes that have taken place over the past 12,000 years, since the time when the Tularosa basin was filled with a large salt lake.

Avoidance is the name of the game when it comes to the White Sands pupfish habitat. We avoided any kind of activity that could potentially harm the fish, the water, or the surrounding vegetation. To maintain the White Sands pupfish habitat, we monitored the water quality, water temperature, and surrounding vegetation, and periodically removed salt cedar, an invasive plant species that absorbs large amounts of water and creates deposits of salt. While these avoidance efforts took place on U.S. Department of Defense land, similar activities regularly occur on corporate land all over the world.

■ Strategy #2: Minimization

For land that is not categorized as an avoidance zone, corporations shift their attention towards minimization strategies that reduce the duration, intensity, and extent of their impacts for biodiversity and wildlife. In this section, we'll highlight four minimization strategies: site selection, operational policies and procedures, wildlife corridors, and green roofs and living walls.

Site Selection

When it comes to developing land, some sites will be better than others from cost, construction, and operations perspectives. Similarly, some sites will be better than others in terms of the impact on biodiversity and wildlife. Using the same biodiversity-assessment data that helped us identify avoidance zones, we can identify and prioritize areas for development and areas where we should take additional steps to minimize environmental impacts.

These impacts to biodiversity and wildlife should be included in the overall evaluation criteria or scorecard that is used to identify where to develop and operate. By doing this, we're more likely to choose a development site that is attractive from construction, operations, and cost perspectives as well as minimizes harm from the perspectives of plants, animals, water, and other natural resources.

For example, Volkswagen of Brazil created a simple tool (an Excel spreadsheet) that shows the biodiversity value of the 25 areas where Volkswagen does business in Brazil and assesses the sustainability of the company's operations. Survey results are scored on a scale of 1 to 10, where 6 or greater is considered a high biodiversity value. Of the 25 Volkswagen sites in Brazil, six were categorized as having a high biodiversity value. The company uses this data to generate ideas on how to integrate its factories with the surrounding landscape from an ecological perspective and provide Volkswagen with new ideas for potential efficiency and cost-saving opportunities.[12]

Operational Policies and Procedures

Once a company chooses one site over another for development, the next step is to determine if a "business-as-usual" approach is appropriate for the new site or if the company should modify its normal processes to minimize impacts to biodiversity and wildlife. These modifications to policies and procedures can take a wide variety of forms.

Let's look at a few examples to provide a better sense of the breadth and scope of the types of policies and procedures that can be implemented to minimize habitat destruction, fragmentation, and degradation.

- **Some companies set goals to reduce the overall footprint of their buildings or operations.** For example, the State Grid Corporation of China has set goals to reduce land use by 10% and reduce construction areas by 20%.[13] One of their strategies was something called an "Electricity Caravan." To transport the material and facilities needed for a project located near the fragile Tibetan plateau of the Sanjiangyuan National Nature Reserve, workers used horse caravans to transport material in this ecologically sensitive area rather than build roads or bridges as is the norm in areas that are not deemed ecologically sensitive.
- **Many companies take steps to avoid certain types of operations or construction activities during the breeding season for birds and other animals in the area.** This precaution helps prevent the destruction of active nests and reduces noise that can scare away or stress animals during the breeding season. For example, some of Cisco Systems' buildings in San Jose, California, are located near a protected area for American cliff swallows. To help protect American cliff swallow habitat during nesting season, Cisco closes its balconies on those buildings and doesn't remove the mud nests until nesting season is over.
- **Many companies set policies that go beyond regulatory compliance.** When I worked as an environmental programs manager at The Coca-Cola Company, Coca-Cola had a policy to follow local regulations or company policy, whatever was more stringent. This policy sometimes translated into significant costs to the company. For example, Coca-Cola treated wastewater to a certain standard prior to discharge into the local body of water, even when it was not required by a country's national or local laws. This sometimes meant that a bottling facility had to install an expensive wastewater-treatment plant to meet the internal requirement. As you can imagine, the idea of cleaning up water before discharging it into an already polluted river was not always well received by bottling plant operators. However, Coca-Cola enforced this policy because it was the right thing to do from an environmental perspective, it set a good example for other local businesses, and it helped build goodwill with government agencies and local communities where it operates.

- **Some companies have created light-abatement policies to prevent unnecessary lighting at night that might impact the behavior of local wildlife.** This policy also has the benefit of reducing energy costs for the site.
- **Some companies implement noise-abatement policies and practices to reduce roadkill.** A mining company—Rio Tinto—educates drivers and enforces strict speed limits to reduce noise and help minimize roadkill at its sites.
- **Many companies have policies to provide environmental education to employees and the local community, which make a positive contribution to sustainable development in the region and reduce human pressure on biodiversity and wildlife.** Volkswagen was the first private sponsor of the Corredor Ecológico de la Sierra Madre Oriental (CESMO) biodiversity corridor in the eastern Sierra Madre Oriental mountain range of Mexico. This 4-million-hectare corridor extends over five Mexican states and is home to around 650 endangered species. As part of this effort, 900 teenagers are being trained as environmental ambassadors to raise environmental and biodiversity awareness and inspire 10,000 young people to participate in conservation activities in the seven nature reserves of the CESMO corridor.[14]

The list goes on and on, but this should give you an idea of the different types of policies and procedures that companies implement to play an important role in protecting biodiversity and wildlife.

Wildlife Corridors

Wildlife corridors are often viewed as a useful tool to help maintain and restore biodiversity and wildlife populations on private and public land. While we'll focus on animals in this section, keep in mind that the corridor concept also applies to plants.

A "wildlife corridor" is defined as any space that facilitates the movement of animals between core habitat fragments. The goal of a corridor is to maintain or improve the number and health of species in an area. This assumes that improving the connectivity of separate patches of a suitable habitat will allow isolated populations of animals to interbreed. Corridors may also help alleviate climate-change impacts on animal populations by enabling animals to move to a more suitable habitat as conditions change. From a human perspective, well-designed corridors help us avoid collisions that kill or injure wildlife and cause property damage and injury to humans.

The importance of wildlife corridors is perhaps best illustrated with an example of large carnivores, such as bears or mountain lions, which require large home ranges for food, den sites, and other needs. To maintain a sustainable population of 50 to 70 mountain lions, we need a minimum of 3,120 square miles; to maintain a sustainable population of 200 black bears, we need at least 780 square miles.[15]

These large habitat requirements are significantly larger than most protected areas in the United States, and that's where corridors can help. Corridors can link large patches of habitat and enable these large carnivores to move from one patch of habitat to another and support a sustainable population of these animals. We could also consider the option of having a smaller population of mountain lions or bears in a certain area, but such small populations of either species are unlikely to be sustainable in the long term.

Corridors come in a wide variety of shapes and sizes. Some corridors take the form of linear patches of land that directly connect two patches of habitat. Other corridors are irregular-shaped stepping stones of land that enable species to move from one patch of habitat to another, even when these stepping stones are not directly connected to the core patches of habitat. Corridors may be man-made, such as underpass tunnels or overpass bridges across a roadway, or they may take the form of natural corridors, such as rivers and mountain ranges.

Some corridors are designed with a regional scale in mind, such as a corridor that facilitates bird and butterfly migration from Canada to Mexico. Other corridors are designed at a local level, perhaps connecting local wetlands to help sustain populations of reptile or amphibian species. For example, Cisco Systems created three turtle tunnels under the highway at its Boxborough, Massachusetts, location to provide safe passage for the migration of Blanding's turtles and eastern box turtles, listed as International Union for Conservation of Nature and Natural Resources (IUCN) Endangered Species and IUCN Vulnerable Species, respectively. Cisco also installed curbing around the site to prevent migrating turtles from entering the roadway and parking areas.

We can design corridors that are intended to be used for brief periods to support seasonal migrations or the dispersal of young animals, or we can design corridors that are intended to be used on a permanent basis. Some species of plants, reptiles, and insects may even spend their entire lives in the corridor habitat.

This brings us to an important point. We've all heard the saying, "Beauty is in the eye of the beholder." This concept also applies to corridors. A corridor that is attractive to one species may be a barrier to another (e.g., a corridor that is appealing to a coyote may not be appealing to a bear, amphibian, otter, or butterfly). It's important to be clear on the target species that the corridor is intended to help before choosing a corridor design.

How does a corporation go about building a corridor for wildlife or plants? Here are the key steps to designing an effective corridor. I've deliberately kept these steps at a high level since the topic could fill a book by itself. Note that corridor analysis and design approaches usually involve modeling and the use of tools, such as a geographic information system (GIS), which are beyond the scope of what we'll cover here. Like most topics, things can quickly become complex, so here is the shortened version.

◆ Step #1: Adopt a linkage mindset.

While this might sound simple, it's probably the most useful and important step of all. Adopt a linkage mindset by considering how your property fits into the bigger picture of linked landscapes and habitats at local, regional, and national levels. Brainstorm about how you could make your company's property as permeable to wildlife as possible. Compared with a perspective focused solely on minimizing habitat fragmentation, a linkage mindset will yield many more creative ideas as you go through the remaining steps. It will also generate more interest and enthusiasm from internal and external stakeholders. You may even want to scrap the term "corridor" and instead call it a "linkage project."

◆ Step #2: Learn more about the core patches of habitat that your corridor will connect.

As you go through Step #1, you may discover that you don't know very much about the bigger picture of connected landscapes and habitats to which you want to link your property. No problem; that's the purpose of this step. Do some research to identify the large pieces of a protected habitat with which your corridor or linkage project is intended to connect, and then learn more about the flora and fauna that live there. A great way to do this is to reach out to the organizations that manage the core habitat patches, including government agencies, nonprofit organizations, tribal representatives, or private land owners.

◆ Step #3: Identify stakeholders and opportunities for partnerships.

Now that you know a bit more about the land with which you'll be connecting, it's time to identify the key stakeholders for your linkage project. You'll want to understand their perspective on potential linkages and look for opportunities to partner with organizations to help you identify the best path forward for your business. The conservation community is generally eager to help design and implement proactive projects that will link habitat for wildlife and plants. Many regional and national efforts are already underway to map and link habitats at state, regional, national, and international levels. Contact your local chapter of The Nature Conservancy, your local wildlife agency, the wildlife or conservation biology faculty at a local university, The Xerces Society (for invertebrates, such as bees and butterflies), or the E. O. Wilson Biodiversity Foundation to connect with experts who can help you identify ways to integrate your land with existing efforts. This may provide a new perspective on how your land integrates with the bigger picture of biodiversity and wildlife conservation for large and small species.

◆ Step #4: Identify your focal species.

In this step, you'll want to work with your project team and local experts to identify eight to 30 focal species that you'll use to help design your linkage project. Your list of focal species will depend on the characteristics of your land, the core habitat to which you are attempting to link, and what lies between your land and the core habitat.

Your list will typically include a variety of predators, prey, mammals, birds, amphibians, reptiles, and insects, which fall into the following three categories:

1. **Area-sensitive species.** These species are the first to disappear when corridors are lost.
2. **Habitat specialists.** These species have the greatest need for continuous swaths of a certain type of vegetation or topographical feature.

3. **Barrier-sensitive species.** These species have a hard time getting across roads, fences, canals, or other barriers between your land and the core habitat.

Even though you're only picking eight to 30 focal species, rest assured that you're not neglecting lesser-known species. The more charismatic "umbrella species" that you've likely selected will serve to represent many of the less glamorous species that also play a vital role in maintaining ecosystem health.

◆ Step #5: Identify the needs of each focal species.

In this step, you'll take your list of eight to 30 focal species and describe the needs of each one. Learn about their habitat requirements, migratory behavior, typical movements within and among habitats, and any successful and failed corridor projects that have been implemented elsewhere. You may also want to contact local experts to help you better understand the needs of the species you've selected.

◆ Step #6: Conduct a cost-benefit assessment to select the final linkage option(s).

Now it's time to identify ways to make your land as attractive and permeable as possible so your focal species will be better connected with the core habitat patches. The outcome of this step is a list of different linkage options, an assessment of how well each option will support permeability for our focal species, and the estimated cost to implement each option.

For the cost estimates, you may want to start with a simple low / medium / high or 1-to-5 scoring system. You can gather actual cost estimates once you have a short list of final candidate options. An effective way to pull this information together is to create a weighted scorecard that lists the different options and the relative score for each one:

	Linkage #1	Linkage #2	Linkage #3	Linkage #4	Linkage #5
Permeability for focal species	Low (1)	Medium (3)	Low (1)	High (5)	High (5)
Ease of implementation	High (5)	Medium (3)	Low (1)	High (5)	Medium (3)
Cost of implementation	High (5)	Medium (3)	Medium (3)	Medium (3)	Low (1)
Totals	11	9	5	13	9

In the above example, Linkage #4 is the best option, followed by Linkage #1. However, if you value certain criteria over others, you may want to add different weights for each of the evaluation criteria. For example, you may want "permeability for focal species" to be weighted 50% while "ease of implementation" and "cost of implementation" are weighted 25% each. In that case, the results would be as follows:

	Linkage #1	Linkage #2	Linkage #3	Linkage #4	Linkage #5
Permeability for focal species (50%)	0.5	1.5	0.5	2.5	2.5
Ease of implementation (25%)	1.25	0.75	0.25	1.25	0.75
Cost of implementation (25%)	1.25	0.75	0.75	0.75	0.25
Totals	3	3	1.5	4.5	3.5

As you can see, by adding weights to the different criteria, Linkage #4 still wins, but Linkage #5 becomes the second-best option. Select evaluation criteria and relative weightings that make sense for your situation.

◆ Step #7: Map your project.

In this step, we draw our final linkage option(s) on a map, typically using GIS software. We may need to conduct additional analyses and field work to validate the models used in the software. This step, particularly the GIS analyses, can be complex, and it's beyond the scope of this book to discuss GIS layers and how to assess movement patterns and permeability using GIS software.

Your goal is to confirm that your linkage project will provide a good habitat for focal species (e.g., food, cover, and nests) and support movement of your focal species among core habitat patches (also known as "permeability") at a reasonable cost. You may need to update your numbers in Step #6 with new values if the GIS analysis provides additional insights into the relative permeability, ease of implementation, or cost of implementation.

◆ Step #8: Design a monitoring and maintenance program.

You'll want to consider one more thing before you plunge into implementing your new linkage project. In this step, you'll develop a monitoring program that will help you evaluate the effectiveness of your habitat linkage, and a maintenance program to keep the land free from exotic species and edge effects, which may impact permeability or habitat quality.

Monitoring and maintenance may add significant costs to the linkage options that you've identified, so you may need to, once again, update your cost and ease of implementation estimates in Step #6. For the monitoring piece, you may want to partner with a local university or nonprofit organization to explore inexpensive ways to monitor the effectiveness of your habitat-linkage efforts, such as through class projects or student research. Researchers may use a variety of mark-recapture and genetic-analysis techniques to evaluate the genetic flow and determine how much a corridor is being used.

◆ Step #9: Implement your final linkage design.

It's finally time to move forward with implementing your habitat-linkage project!

Implementing Corridors as a Profitable-Conservation Strategy

Now that you've seen the amount of time and effort required to implement a corridor, you're probably asking yourself two important questions: "Do corridors work?" and "What is the financial return for creating habitat linkages?" Unfortunately, as is often the case for value-proposition questions, the answer is, "It depends."

For the return on investment (ROI) question, it depends on how you calculate your project's costs and benefits. The costs are relatively easy to calculate, although they'll vary based on the land you own, the land that surrounds you, and the type of linkage projects you implement. When calculating benefits, that's where things get a bit fuzzy. From a business perspective, the benefits of habitat linkages usually come in the form of intangibles, such as employee satisfaction and enhanced reputation and goodwill among customers, consumers, and regulators. In some cases, your linkage project may yield more tangible benefits, such as providing the opportunity to conduct operations in one area in exchange for protecting habitat or creating linkages in other, higher-priority conservation areas. This is a concept that we'll explore later in the "Strategy #4: Biodiversity Offsets and Voluntary Compensatory Actions" section of this chapter.

The short answer to "Do corridors work?" is that wildlife corridors have yielded mixed results. Some linkages have provided tangible benefits to wildlife and plants while other corridors have been a flop. Studies are underway that hope to shed some light on the effectiveness of wildlife corridors from gene-flow and species-diversity perspectives, but the jury is still out.

While some large land owners may have viable opportunities to implement successful wildlife-corridor projects, most businesses won't need to go down that path. Instead, most companies can simply implement Step #1 ("Adopt a linkage mindset.") and look for ways to make their land more permeable to native wildlife in the area. This approach typically yields simple projects that involve planting native vegetation, removing invasive species, and providing water sources that are attractive to local insect pollinators, birds, amphibians, reptiles, and mammals.

Some companies pursue interesting variations of the linkage concept in the form of green roofs, living walls, and green infrastructure that often yield a positive, quantifiable ROI.

Green Roofs and Living Walls

Green roofs and living walls may be viewed as a type of wildlife corridor that is beneficial for species, such as insects and birds, and can boost the bottom line for business. Corporations reap tangible benefits from energy savings, reductions in stormwater runoff, and noise abatement, as well as intangible benefits like employee satisfaction and customer goodwill.

A "green roof" (also known as a "living roof") is a roof of a building that is partially or completely covered with vegetation. You can think of a living wall as a vertical garden, where plants are rooted in a structural support that is fastened to a wall.

Green roofs come in three flavors: extensive, intensive, and semi-extensive. These three types of green roofs are distinguished primarily by the amount of substrate, or growing medium, that is used to keep plants in place and provide an environment for the root system to function.

Here are the key characteristics of the three types of green roofs:

- **Extensive.** Extensive green roofs have a shallow substrate that is typically less than 6 inches in depth. These lightweight, low-maintenance systems are primarily composed of vegetation, such as grass or moss, with areas that are not designed to be accessed by people on a regular basis. If an irrigation system is installed, then maintenance is relatively simple, requiring just a few visits per year to fertilize the plants, remove weeds, and ensure that the roof is stable. Nonirrigated systems will require additional visits to water the plants.
- **Intensive.** Intensive green roofs have a substrate depth that exceeds 6 inches, with some roof substrate layers exceeding 3 feet in depth. This deep-growing medium can support a wide variety of plants and trees, which can weigh as much as 200 pounds per square foot when watered. Compared with extensive roofs, intensive roofs pro-

vide better insulation, stormwater management, and biodiversity potential. These roofs are often designed to be regularly accessed and used by people as a place to relax and enjoy. On the down side, intensive roofs may require a significant amount of maintenance, depending on the type of vegetation that is planted.

- **Semi-extensive.** As you might expect, semi-extensive green roofs fall somewhere between extensive and intensive systems, with a substrate depth of around 6 inches. These roofs support a broader variety of plants compared to an extensive system, but they can't support the large trees and plants that you might find in an intensive system. Semi-extensive roofs attempt to strike a balance, making trade-offs among weight, maintenance, insulation, biodiversity potential, stormwater management, and the provision of a desirable environment in which employees can socialize.

Regardless of the type of green roof you choose, a typical roof will include the following components:

- **Waterproof membrane.** Waterproof membranes are a critical component for any green roof. It's important to select a material that is resistant to root penetration, unless you enjoy fixing water leaks through the roof!
- **Root barrier.** The root barrier can be a chemical or a physical barrier that helps prevent roots from damaging the waterproof membrane.
- **Drainage layer.** Drainage is one of the most important factors to consider in setting up a green roof. The drainage layer enables stormwater to drain without washing away the substrate. The best drainage material options depend on the type of vegetation that is planted on the roof, the amount of moisture that needs to be retained, and the rainfall patterns that your site experiences.
- **Filter course.** Filter course is a type of geo-textile layer used to separate the drainage layer from the actual substrate or growing medium. Filter course helps prevent soil and particulates from being washed away from the growing medium.
- **Substrate or growing medium.** The substrate or growing medium can take the form of a pre-engineered mix or a custom design for your green roof. Since weight is a critical factor to consider in the design of a green roof, you'll want to pay close attention to the

water-retention capacity of the different substrate options that you have. To play it safe, it's best to use the full-water holding capacity for each substrate in your weight calculations.

If that sounds complicated and difficult, keep in mind that there are also modular systems, which come fully planted in self-contained trays. Simply place the trays anywhere you like, although you'll still want to include a waterproof membrane under the trays.

Now that we've learned the basics of what a green roof is, let's briefly introduce green walls. "Green walls" (also known as "living walls") are usually simpler than a green roof, can be found indoors or outdoors, and are vertical rather than horizontal.

These vertical gardens fall into two categories:

1. **Green façades.** A green-façade system uses climbing plants or cascading ground covers that grow from the ground and climb up or down a structure, such as a trellis or container, creating a living wall.
2. **Green walls.** A green wall consists of prevegetated panels or modular green walls that are attached directly to the wall or fixed inside of a structural framework. The vegetated mat walls contain a growing medium and perforations to plant the vegetation.

If you do an internet search for "green roof" or "green wall," you'll find many examples to help you visualize what this looks like in both residential and business settings. One particularly striking example is the ACROS Fukuoka Prefectural International Hall (ACROS is short for "Asian Crossroads Over the Sea") in the city center of Fukuoka, Japan. Constructed in 1995, the ACROS building includes an intensive green-roof system designed to connect with adjacent Tenjin Central Park and is accessible to the public. The architect who designed the building—Emilio Ambasz—was awarded the project because he was able to reconcile two competing desires: doubling the size of Tenjin Central Park, which is the only green open space in that part of the city, and providing a powerful, symbolic building in the city center of Fukuoka.

The ACROS green roof has a substrate depth that varies between 12 and 24 inches. When first constructed, there were 37,000 plants that represent 76 plant species. Today, thanks to birds and other animals that have brought in seeds, there are now 50,000 plants that represent 120 plant species.[16] It's a great example of how a building can contribute to the natural biodiversity of a region and how wildlife can cultivate the vegetation on a roof just as they would in a natural system.

The insulating properties of the ACROS green roof have reduced the heat-island effect in the area, which translates into reduced energy costs and carbon dioxide emissions. One study found a 15-degree C difference among the surface temperatures of concrete in the area, concluding that the green roof suppressed a rise in the surrounding air temperature.[17]

Studies of green roofs have found that they often become a habitat for soil organisms, such as mites, springtails, bacteria, and fungi, which play a critical role in nutrient cycling and sustainable plant growth. Given that these species don't fly, how do they get there? It turns out that many organisms either hitch a ride with birds or ride air currents as "aerial plankton." Some of the organisms arrive as part of the original building materials.

However, one study found that many of the organisms that are part of the original soil community in construction materials die soon after the roof is constructed due to harsh rooftop environments with high winds, temperature extremes, and drought-like conditions. The study emphasizes the importance of selecting the proper soil community in the construction materials to help ensure that the roof is sustainable in the long term.[18] In addition, it may be useful to combine green roofs with living walls to connect the green roof with organisms that live in ground-level soil communities.

Profitability of Installing Green Roofs and Living Walls

All of this sounds great, but are green roofs and living walls a profitable-conservation strategy?

The short answer is, "Yes."

Well-designed green roofs and living walls have the potential to yield significant benefits for both companies and the environment. They can:

- Mitigate the heat-island effect in cities
- Reduce the amount of energy required to operate heating and cooling systems within a building
- Reduce air pollution and greenhouse-gas emissions
- Improve stormwater management and water quality
- Enhance the aesthetics and property value of a building

- Increase the amount of usable space for building occupants
- Reduce the amount of noise in an urban environment
- Improve employee satisfaction
- Provide a habitat for many species of insects, birds, and other animals

Many of these benefits can help a business reduce expenses. The biggest cost savings usually come in the form of reduced heating and cooling bills, since green roofs provide insulation in the winter and a cooling effect in the summer. The amount of savings will vary, depending on your climate and local utility costs.

Let's look at data collected from several studies to help us quantify the benefits of green roofs:

- The National Research Council Canada claims that a green roof can reduce air-conditioning demand in the summer by as much as 75%, with exposed roofs reaching temperatures as high as 158 degrees F, while a green roof heats to just 77 degrees F.[19]
- The American Society of Landscape Architects retrofitted a green roof at its Washington, DC, headquarters, which resulted in a 10% energy savings in winter and a few percentage points of savings in the summer. The green roof was found to be as much as 43.5 degrees cooler than conventional black roofs on neighboring buildings.[20]
- A University of Michigan study compared the expected costs and benefits of conventional roofs with a 21,000-square-foot green roof. The university concluded that the green roof would cost US$ 464,000 to install, compared to US$ 335,000 for a conventional roof (in 2006). However, the green roof would save roughly US$ 200,000 over the life of the roof, with two-thirds of the cost savings coming from reduced energy needs.[21]
- Studies in Germany found that roofs with built-up membrane systems can have a life expectancy at least twice, and usually three times, longer than a standard roof by protecting it from sun, rain, snow, hail, and dust.[22]

- Building owners can recoup the cost of the green roof in as little as five to six years, thanks to a combination of energy savings and stormwater-control savings. Many cities offer tax and fee incentives to install a green roof because a typical green roof absorbs 45% to 60% of rainfall on average, which can save a city millions of dollars in stormwater-infrastructure improvements.[23]
- Green roofs have been shown to improve the market value of a building, particularly for residential buildings. In an assessment conducted in Australia, green roofs that include living spaces and access to gardens for apartment tenants improved the market value of those apartments by an estimated 10%.[24]
- Ford Motor Company's River Rouge plant in Dearborn, Michigan, has one of the largest expanses of extensive green roof, with 450,000 square feet of assembly plant roofs covered with sedum and other plants. The drought-resistant species of sedum have attracted 35 insect, spider, and bird species, and 11 plant species. Within five days of the green roof being installed, local killdeer had nested and laid eggs in the sedum. The US$ 15 million project enabled Ford Motor Company to avoid US$ 50 million worth of mechanical treatment facilities on-site.[25]
- The U.S. Postal Service's Morgan facility has the largest green roof in New York City, and it's also one of the largest green roofs in the country. Constructed in 2008, the 2.5-acre (108,900-square-foot) green roof includes 25 low-growing plant species that are never watered, weeded, or fertilized, yet have proved to reduce the building's stormwater runoff by as much as 75% in the summer and 40% in the winter. The U.S. Postal Service estimates that the green roof reduces the building's energy costs by US$ 30,000 per year.[26]

Many more studies are underway to look at the long-term costs and benefits of installing green roofs and living walls. In the meantime, plenty of companies have already taken the plunge, which is a good indicator that green roofs are viewed as a profitable-conservation strategy by these companies. As you'll see in the Chapter 10 case study, Walmart has installed green roofs at many of its facilities, and the company has collected useful data in assessing the economic viability of green roofs at various locations.

Here are some other examples of companies that have installed green roofs:

- A few years ago, Facebook installed a 9-acre green roof that includes more than 400 trees and a half-mile walking trail on one of its buildings at the company's Menlo Park, California, headquarters.[27]
- In 2015, Macy's installed the Corporate Headquarters Habitat Roof, which is a 16,000-square-foot, semi-intensive roof in Cincinnati, Ohio. The Habitat Roof includes a variety of plants that were carefully selected to provide nectar and a habitat for butterflies and other pollinators. The roof is now registered as a Monarch Way Station and a Wildlife Habitat.[28]
- Timber and forest products company Weyerhaeuser was an early adopter of the green-roof concept. Back in 1971, they installed a 358,000-square-foot roof system at its corporate headquarters building in Federal Way, Washington before selling the buildings a few years ago to move the headquarters from the suburbs to the city of Seattle. The five-story roof system included a series of stepped terraces covered in vegetation, which created the appearance of blending into the surrounding landscape when viewed from the air.[29]

While we're on the topic of early adopters, Germany has been implementing green roofs for over 100 years, although the concept didn't really take off until the 1970s. Today, Germany has the largest number of green roofs in the world, and it's considered to have the most advanced knowledge of modern green-roof technology. Ten percent of the roofs in Germany are now green roofs, and approximately 86,000,000 square feet of new green roofs are being constructed in Germany each year.[30] In cities like Stuttgart, nearly 25% of the city's flat roofs are green roofs, thanks to a combination of tax abatements, government incentives, and regulations that mandate green roofs for most new construction. Nearly one-third of all German cities have regulations to support green-roof and rainwater technology.[31]

Other countries are starting to jump on the green-roof bandwagon as well. In Canada, Toronto recently became the first city in the Western Hemisphere to mandate green roofs. The mandate was put in place after a 2005 study, which concluded that Toronto could save nearly US$ 30 million a year on stormwater management, energy costs, and costs related to urban heat-island effects.[32] Toronto requires all new buildings with a total floor area greater than 21,257 square feet to cover 20% to 60% of their roofs with vegetation, depending on the size of the building.[33] Green roofs are also sprouting up across Australia and Asia, with new green-roof projects being implemented in China, Singapore, Japan, the Philippines, and Vietnam. Clearly, green roofs are deemed to have a positive ROI by the companies that are implementing these projects.

From a biodiversity perspective, an interesting experimental green-roof project is underway in Berlin, Germany, where the roof was designed specifically to help protect biodiversity. The International Garden Exhibition in Berlin (also known as "IGA Berlin 2017") included a visitor center with a 2,000-square-meter (21,528-square-foot) extensive green roof that provides foraging opportunities and shelter for wild bees, butterflies, beetles, birds, and a variety of other species. This biodiverse green-roof project will serve as an important reference point and inspiration for those interested in installing new green roofs or upgrading existing green roofs to support a greater variety of wildlife species.

Here are some of the key approaches with which IGA Berlin 2017 is experimenting to create a green roof that supports greater species diversity:

- **Variety of substrate depths.** A variety of substrate depths enables the roof to support a wider variety of plant species. Low-growing and low-maintenance sedums and other succulent plants were planted in relatively shallow substrate depths of 6 centimeters (2.4 inches), while species of grasses and herbs were planted in substrate depths of up to 15 centimeters (5.9 inches) to provide more room for their roots.
- **Higher-quality substrate.** The typical nutrient-poor soil used for extensive green roofs was enriched with organic substrate to provide nutrients, which better support the diversity of vegetation that was planted on the roof.
- **Variety of substrate surfaces.** The roof includes a varied assortment of substrate surfaces and features, such as the following:
    - **Vegetation-free areas.** Some areas of the roof are deliberately vegetation-free and instead contain sand islands and clay and gravel beds, which provide important supplementary habitats for invertebrates for breeding, sunning, and shelter. The sand beds are intended to attract sand-breeding insects, such as digger wasps and sand bees. The clay is used as building material

by insects and birds, and the gravel is used as cover by spiders and beetles.

- **Temporary water features.** In some areas of the roof, pieces of membrane have been covered with sand to retain rainwater for longer periods. These areas are expected to provide more water for insects and birds.
- **Elevated areas with food plants.** The roof includes elevated areas that contain food plants for foraging insects. Food plants include precultivated, herbaceous perennials and an herb-and-grass seed mixture. The roof climate is like a natural, dry grassland, so the roof includes plants that you would find in that type of habitat.
- **Nesting aids for insects.** A variety of nesting aids have been installed on the roof to attract permanent insect colonies, including insect hotels for wild bees and parasitic wasps, nest boxes for bumble bees, and pits for ants.
- **Log piles and deadwood.** Dead branches and logs have been added to the roof to provide valuable structural elements, which serve as habitats for moss, lichen, fungi, invertebrates, flies, mosquitoes, ants, solitary wild bees, and wasps. The wood piles are also used by birds to perch, hide, sing, and feed. These features are expected to provide species-rich and ecologically valuable habitats over time.

In the coming years, the Technical University of Berlin will be monitoring the green-roof project and documenting the results. This will include a cost-benefit analysis, which compares the costs of installation and maintenance with a valuation of the ecosystem services that are provided by the biodiverse roof habitat.

As green-roof technology continues to improve, and long-term study data are collected and analyzed, it's likely that green roofs and living walls will continue to increase in popularity for both residential and corporate buildings all over the world. From a biodiversity perspective, particularly for insect pollinators and other small animal species, these efforts may partly compensate for green spaces that have been lost due to development activities.

Strategy #3: Rehabilitation and Restoration

We've looked at two general strategies that companies can implement to address habitat destruction and fragmentation: avoidance and minimization. In situations where avoidance and minimization are not practical or feasible, companies may turn to a third strategy: rehabilitation and restoration. With this strategy, a company attempts to rehabilitate degraded ecosystems or restore cleared ecosystems in areas that have previously been cleared, developed, or neglected.

There is often some confusion around the terms "remediation," "rehabilitation," and "restoration," so let's start with a few definitions. Remediation refers to the process of reducing or stopping pollution that threatens the health of people or wildlife. Once we've completed the removal and cleanup of pollution, we can then begin talking about rehabilitation or restoration. Rehabilitation is the process of repairing ecosystem processes but not to the pre-existing, historical trajectory of the ecosystem. Restoration, on the other hand, is the process of recovering an ecosystem that has been damaged or destroyed and returning it to its historical trajectory.

Rehabilitation and restoration is commonly used in industries such as mining and oil and gas. Companies will re-establish forest and grassland communities in areas that had been cleared for operations by replacing topsoil (where the original topsoil is typically stored during operations) and planting appropriate native species. Restoration activities may also occur in areas adjacent to avoidance zones, which provides a buffer, improves connectivity, and recolonizes native plant and wildlife species.

According to the World Resources Institute, there are many opportunities for restoration. Roughly one-quarter of the world's land mass has been subject to environmental degradation over the past 50 years at an estimated cost of US$ 6.3 trillion in lost ecosystem services.[34]

Even though there are opportunities for land restoration, the business case is not always attractive due to the extended time horizon (i.e., 10 to 20 years) for restoration projects. In addition, government incentives are not always aligned with rehabilitation and restoration efforts. Despite this reality, some industries are encouraged, and sometimes required, to implement a rehabilitation and restoration strategy to get permission to operate in certain areas. Even when rehabilitation and restoration are not required, it can be an effective risk-management strategy that is well received by regulators, customers, employees, and the local community.

We'll revisit the topic of rehabilitation and restoration in Chapter 4, which covers invasive species and native vegetation, since many of the rehabilitation and restoration activities involve planting native species and removing invasive species.

■ Strategy #4: Biodiversity Offsets and Voluntary Compensatory Actions

Biodiversity offsets are a fourth strategy that companies may pursue to address habitat destruction and fragmentation. The concept of a biodiversity offset is relatively simple. A company has a proposed project that will result in negative impacts to biodiversity at the target site. To offset that loss, the company enters an agreement to protect biodiversity at another site. The result is no net loss of biodiversity or, preferably, a net gain of biodiversity from the perspective of species composition, habitat structure, ecosystem function, and cultural values of biodiversity.

If you're looking for a more formal definition, we can turn to a document titled *Independent report on biodiversity offsets*, which was commissioned in 2012 through a partnership between the International Council on Mining & Metals and IUCN. In that document, biodiversity offsets are defined as follows:

> "Biodiversity offsets are measurable conservation outcomes resulting from actions designed to compensate for significant residual adverse biodiversity impacts arising from development plans or projects after appropriate prevention and mitigation measures have been taken."[35]

Biodiversity offsets differ from philanthropic donations and other compensatory actions by linking the offset to the biodiversity impacts of a specific project. To make this point clearer, let's look at an example from Walmart.

Walmart has a goal to conserve 1 acre of wildlife habitat for every acre of land developed by Walmart stores. In practice, Walmart's Acres for America program has resulted in a 10:1 ratio of conservation to development.[36] This, of course, is a good thing for wildlife. The conservation value of the land purchased through the Acres for America program is assumed to be greater than the conservation value of the land that Walmart is developing for its stores.

Walmart's approach has one significant difference from a biodiversity offset: There's no formal link between the actual biodiversity impacts of the company's development activities and the biodiversity gains from purchasing land for conservation. Walmart simply looks at the overall footprint of land developed for new stores and ensures that the company protects at least that many acres for conservation. The company does not assess the type, scale, or amount of biodiversity lost and gained from each development project and land-conservation purchase.

Biodiversity offsets take the Walmart "acres-for-acres" conservation approach a step further by formally requiring no net loss of the biodiversity value of the land. Ideally, the goal is to obtain a positive net gain of biodiversity value from the transaction. The downside of biodiversity offsets is that they are more complex and expensive to implement. The costs and resources required to do a biodiversity offset can make traditional philanthropy and "acres-for-acres" conservation approaches more appealing and a better fit with stakeholder expectations, depending on the company, industry, and location.

Value Proposition of Biodiversity Offsets

Given the higher cost and complexity of biodiversity offsets, why would companies want to pursue this strategy? For starters, many stakeholders like the transparent and quantitative nature of biodiversity offsets, and it can help ease "greenwashing" claims. However, the primary driver is the fact that biodiversity offsets are considered favorable by many lending and regulatory agencies around the world. In some cases, biodiversity offsets are a required cost of doing business.

For example, corporations often look for loans to get money to support new development projects. Some lenders have decided to incorporate International Finance Corporation Performance Standard 6 (IFC PS6) in their loan agreements. IFC PS6 includes the following requirement:

> "For the protection and conservation of biodiversity, the mitigation hierarchy includes biodiversity offsets, which may be considered only after appropriate avoidance, minimization, and restoration measures have been applied. A biodiversity offset should be designed and implemented to achieve measurable conservation outcomes that can reasonably be expected to result

> in no net loss and preferably a net gain of biodiversity; however, a net gain is required in critical habitats. The design of a biodiversity offset must adhere to the 'like-for-like or better' principle and must be carried out in alignment with best available information and current practices. When a client is considering the development of an offset as part of the mitigation strategy, external experts with knowledge in offset design and implementation must be involved."[37]

That's a mouthful, but the takeaway is that, if the company wants a loan, then a biodiversity offset may be required. The other important takeaway is that biodiversity offsets should only be considered after avoidance, minimization, and restoration measures have been applied.

Financial institutions aren't the only ones requiring biodiversity offsets. More and more government agencies around the world are passing legislation that includes biodiversity offsets as a potential or required approach for balancing development and conservation. Part of the motivation behind this legislation is that some government agencies want to use industry money to help them achieve national conservation targets to which they have already committed, such as the terms specified in the Convention on Biological Diversity. Some scientists and environmental organizations don't like this approach as it implies that the country was not going to meet its pre-existing commitments without the biodiversity-offset projects. To address this concern, they recommend that future conservation agreements should explicitly require separate accounting for protected areas that are created from offset projects.

Implementation of a Biodiversity-Offset Project

Now that we have some background on the topic, let's look at how companies implement biodiversity offsets in practice. As usual, things can get complex when we explore the details, so we'll keep things at a high level.

◆ Step #1: Ensure that you've done everything you can from avoidance, minimization, and restoration perspectives.

Consider this step to be a friendly reminder that biodiversity offsets should be viewed as a last-resort strategy. Biodiversity offsets should only be considered after taking all reasonable measures to avoid, minimize, and restore habitat in the areas of concern. In this step, we confirm that avoidance, minimization, and restoration strategies are no longer viable options.

◆ Step #2: Identify and engage with your stakeholders.

We've identified the land that is going to be developed and made the decision to pursue the last-resort strategy of a biodiversity offset. Now it's time to identify and engage with the stakeholders who will play a role in the proposed biodiversity-offset project:

- **Government / regulatory agency.** This entity is required by law to regulate and oversee the biodiversity offset. Depending on your location and the scope of your project, you may need to work with multiple regulatory agencies.
- **Project developer / offset buyer.** This would be you, assuming you're associated with the company that would like to pursue a biodiversity-offset project.
- **Offset seller.** This is a private or public entity that creates offsets. It can take the form of nongovernmental organizations (NGOs), government agencies, environmental consultants, lawyers, engineers, and private mitigation bankers.
- **Offset provider.** This is the owner or manager of the land that you hope to purchase to offset the impacts of your development project. This can be an NGO, a private land owner, or a local council.
- **Affected community.** This is the local population in the area that is impacted by your biodiversity-offset project.

Early in the process, you'll want to engage with the appropriate stakeholders to ensure that the offsets are appropriately designed, taking into consideration local, regional, and international standards and values. Standards like IFC PS6 detail specific requirements, such as the need to consult with affected communities to hear their views on the proposed offset, so you'll want to read up on the details of any standard that you intend to follow.

◆ Step #3: Select and prioritize the biodiversity- and ecosystem-service features to include in the offset analysis.

In this step, you'll work with appropriate stakeholders to help you identify and prioritize the different biodiversity- and ecosystem-service features to include in your offset analysis. You'll find that different stakeholders will value different aspects of biodiversity, so be sure to gather a broad range of stakeholder input. Once you've gathered a list of biodiversity- and ecosystem-service features, you'll need to prioritize the features and determine which ones to include in the scope of your offset project and which features to mitigate through other means.

The output of Step #3 is a biodiversity-values matrix, which looks at biodiversity, ecosystem services, economic values, and cultural values from the vantage point of three filters: species, habitats and sites, and ecosystem processes. Your table columns should include the major components of biodiversity (i.e., species, habitats and sites, and cultural values), and the rows should include the ecosystem services and other value derived from biodiversity as well as the intrinsic value of biodiversity itself.

◆ Step #4: Select the appropriate data-collection methods for the offset analysis and collect the data.

Now that you've defined the scope of the offset, it's time to choose an appropriate data-collection methodology that you'll use to measure the biodiversity features and ecosystem services that are within your scope.

You'll inevitably come across some features that will cause you to say, "How in the heck can I measure that?" This is part of the fun!

You may need to partner with stakeholders and subject-matter experts to develop surrogate measures and collect data for some of the biodiversity features of interest. For example, if you've identified a species of bird as one of your high-priority biodiversity features that you wish to measure, then you may want to work with experts who will suggest field-survey methods to either count the number of birds directly or use surrogate measures, such as the number of acres of suitable forest habitat and the number of nests or tree holes for that species of bird. In some cases, the regulatory agency or financial institution standard, such as IFC PS6, will take the guess work out of it by specifying the data-collection methods that you'll need to use. Be sure to first check with your regulatory agencies and lenders. They may require using specific "currencies" to compare the impacted land with the offset land.

◆ Step #5: Convert the data into agreed-upon currencies or measures that facilitate comparison.

In this step, we convert our measures into currencies, which will enable us to make comparisons between the gains and losses of the impacted land and the offset land. These metrics are referred to as "currencies" since they provide a common unit of losses and gains that we can trade or exchange.

One common type of biodiversity offset currency used is Extent x Condition, where the number of acres of a specific habitat type or vegetation community is multiplied by a measure of the condition of the habitat. For example, we may calculate "number of acres multiplied by the percentage of forest canopy cover" and use that number as our currency. Using this method, 100 acres of a habitat with 50% forest canopy cover would yield a value of 50 habitat acres available for trade or exchange.

The definition of currencies is a critical step since these currencies will be representing biodiversity for your project. Some regulatory agencies and financial lending standards will specify the mandatory currencies you'll need to use. This step helps minimize the risk of using currencies that don't adequately reflect the true biodiversity value of developed land.

◆ Step #6: Reach an agreement on key technical principles for the biodiversity offset and adjust the proposed offset design as needed.

At this point, you've selected the appropriate methods for data collection, collected the necessary data, and converted the data into agreed-upon currencies for exchange, but you're not done yet! You still need to reach an agreement on some key technical principles that will guide your biodiversity-offset project. It's likely that you've already reached an agreement on many of these topics through your stakeholder-engagement activities in the previous steps, but don't be surprised if key stakeholders want to revisit some key technical principles now that you've collected data and defined currencies.

You may be asked to make some adjustments to your proposed biodiversity offset after reviewing and discussing these following four technical principles:

1. **Limits to offsetting.** For any proposed biodiversity-offset project, we need to recognize that there are limits to what can be offset. Some losses are impossible to offset. For example, if the proposed project will wipe out the last remaining population of an endangered species so that the species will be extinct in the wild, it's clear that your biodiversity-offset proposal should not move forward. There are limits to what can be considered appropriate for a biodiversity offset. The justification for limits to a biodiversity offset are based on three factors: the uniqueness of the biodiversity feature, quantitative thresholds of irreplaceability or vulnerability of a critical habitat or extinction risk, and national conservation-planning targets that function as caps. It can be challenging to reach an agreement on defining the limits of what can be offset, but there are resources (e.g., regional or national conservation plans and IFC PS6) that can help.
2. **Additionality.** The condition of additionality states that the biodiversity gains must result directly from the conservation actions that are financed through the offset. The condition of additionality is not met if the offset funding is used to protect areas that already receive sufficient funding from government programs. Similarly, additionality is not met if the offset land is not threatened or undergoing degradation or if there are existing incentives or actions in place for landowners to manage the land for biodiversity.
3. **Equivalency.** The condition of equivalency aims to determine if the biodiversity offset is a fair exchange. Given the fact that no two areas are ecologically identical, the topic of equivalency can be a sticky subject. Equivalency requires some quantitative measurements of the various types of losses and gains to biodiversity from the perspectives of type, amount, time, and space.
    - **Type.** "Equivalency in the type of biodiversity" means that the biodiversity gains at the offset site need to include the same types of species, habitats, ecosystems, or ecological functions as

the developed site. This can be evaluated using a matrix that compares the key biodiversity values or components between the offset site and the developed site.

- **Amount.** "Equivalency in the amount of biodiversity" means that there is an equivalent amount of biodiversity gains and losses from the transaction. The gains and losses can be measured by comparing habitat acreage and species population sizes.
- **Time.** "Equivalency in time" focuses on the timing of biodiversity losses and gains. An offset site that will achieve its goals 100 years from now will not be worth the same to stakeholders as intact land that exists today. Ecosystem services often come into play when we talk about time. For example, if a local community will lose access to land for hunting, fishing, firewood, and medicinal plants for 10 to 20 years, this could drastically impact the local economy and community. Similarly, if the land serves as an important migratory stopover site for birds or other species, then the loss of that habitat for 10 to 20 years could cause significant long-term damage to those animal populations. For these reasons, it's usually best to ensure that the offset land and any other mitigations are in place prior to developing the impacted land. If you are doing financial net-present-value calculations, you'll want to include time discounting in any habitat- and resource-equivalency analyses that are performed.
- **Space.** "Equivalency in space" looks at how near the offset site is to the impact site. Nearby sites are more likely to include similar habitats and species. A geographic link between the loss site and offset site is typically preferred by stakeholders and is often a regulatory requirement. A geographic link may take the form of a shared watershed, a bioregion, an ecological network, a state, a province, or a nation. In practice, we may find that the best site for a biodiversity offset may not be the closest one to the impact site for a variety of social, political, or biological reasons. It's helpful to refer to existing national and regional conservation plans to identify the best offset location for your project.

4. **Permanence.** To meet the condition of permanence, gains and impacts need to last for the same amount of time. Companies may accomplish this by formally registering biodiversity offsets as legal protected areas or forming other land-tenure agreements.

◆ Step #7: Offset implementation and monitoring

You made it! As you can see, it takes quite a bit of prep work before you can proceed with a biodiversity-offset project. This implementation approach is often specified by regulatory agencies or offset suppliers, such as land trusts, NGOs, and other businesses. The agreement you reach may include conservation easements, ecological restoration, improved conservation management of the offset land, and the control of hunting and invasive species.

Once the biodiversity offset project is in place, you may be expected to monitor and actively manage the offset land to ensure that its conservation value is maintained. Many corporations choose to partner with government agencies or conservation NGOs for assistance in managing the offset as a protected area. To address concerns about permanence, you may decide to formally change land tenure so that the offset land is formally registered as a legally protected area. These are just a few of the considerations that you may wish to explore with regulatory agencies and offset suppliers.

Biodiversity Offsets as a Profitable-Conservation Strategy

Biodiversity offsets have the potential to be profitable for both business and the environment, but the devil's in the details. From a business perspective, biodiversity offsets enable corporations to operate in areas that yield significant revenues for the company while mitigating the risk of negative responses from the local community, customers, consumers, lenders, regulatory agencies, and other stakeholders. From an environmental perspective, biodiversity offsets have the potential to yield a net gain for biodiversity. However, as we have already seen in this section, biodiversity gains depend on factors such as the equivalency of the offset, the number of acres and size of species populations that are protected, the timing of the biodiversity gains and losses, and the proximity of the offset site to the target site.

Critics of biodiversity offsets argue that they enable developers to buy their way out of conservation requirements. Another criticism that we touched on earlier is that biodiversity offsets may enable governments to avoid meeting pre-existing conservation commitments and targets. These are certainly valid concerns. Despite these criticisms, current trends suggest that biodiversity offsets will continue to increase in popularity. When done properly, biodiversity offsets can serve as an important piece of the puzzle to help minimize biodiversity loss on Earth by protecting biodiversity hotspots that have been identified from a landscape scale or *Half-Earth* perspective.

Conclusion

Whew! That was a long chapter but an important one. I hope you learned a few things about the important topic of habitat destruction and what corporations can do to address the issue. More importantly, I hope you have a few ideas percolating in your head with which you'll experiment.

Chapter 3 Action Steps

1. Describe how your organization avoids, minimizes, restores, and offsets impacts to biodiversity and wildlife from the perspectives of habitat destruction and fragmentation.
2. Has your company conducted a biodiversity assessment to help you identify and map areas to avoid and minimize impacts? If not, then why not?
3. Adopting a linkage mindset, what steps could you take to make your organization's property as permeable to wildlife as possible?
4. Are green roofs a profitable-conservation strategy for your business? Why or why not?

Chapter 3 Endnotes

1. Edward O. Wilson, *Half-Earth: Our Planet's Fight for Life* (New York: Liveright, 2017), 53.
2. World Wildlife Fund, "Deforestation." Accessed June 4, 2018. https://www.worldwildlife.org/threats/deforestation.
3. Ibid.
4. Ibid.
5. Note 1, supra, 182.
6. Jodi A. Hilty, William Z. Lidicker, Jr., and Adina M. Merenlender, *Corridor Ecology: The Science and Practice of Linking Landscapes for Biodiversity Conservation* (Washington, DC: Island Press, 2006), 127–128.
7. Doug Kreutz, "Roadkill numbers huge at Saguaro Park, officials say," Arizona Daily Star, February 11, 2013.
8. Jessica Aldred, "The final wave of the Panamanian golden frog." The Guardian. September 3, 2012. Accessed June 5, 2018. https://www.theguardian.com/environment/2012/sep/03/panamanian-golden-frog.
9. J. B. Ruhl (1998). "Endangered Species Act and Private Property: A Matter of Timing and Location," Cornell Journal of Law and Public Policy: Vol. 8: Iss. 1, Article 2, 38. http://scholarship.law.cornell.edu/cjlpp/vol8/iss1/2.
10. B. Conrod (2004). "Highlights: Last African oryx removed from White Sands National Monument." Park Science 22(2), Fall 2004 (ISSN 1090-9966, National Park Service, U.S. Department of the Interior). National Parks Service. Accessed June 5, 2018. https://nature.nps.gov/parkscience/index.cfm?ArticleID=144&ArticleTypeID=4.
11. Ibid.
12. Volkswagen AG, "Brazil." Volkswagen Sustainability Report—CSR Projects—Brazil. Accessed February 5, 2017. https://csrprojects.volkswagenag.com/csr-projects/brazil.html#0,1,2,3,4,5,6,7,8,9,10/8/0,1,2,3,4,5,6,7,8,9,10,11,12,13,14.
13. State Grid Corporation of China, "Corporate Social Responsibility Report 2015," 60.
14. Volkswagen AG, "Mexico." Volkswagen Sustainability Report—CSR Projects—Brazil. Accessed March 7, 2017. https://csrprojects.volkswagenag.com/csr-projects/mexiko.html#0,1,2,3,4,5,6,7,8,9,10/6/0,1,2,3,4,5,6,7,8,9,10,11,12,13,14.
15. Note 6, supra, 24–25.

16. "Greenroofs.com Projects—ACROS Fukuoka Prefectural International Hall." SOLARIS at Fusionopolis (Phase 2B): From Military Base to Bioclimatic Eco-Architecture, By T. R. Hamzah & Yeang Sdn. Bhd. Accessed June 8, 2018. http://www.greenroofs.com/projects/pview.php?id=476.

17. Ibid.

18. Heather Rumble, Paul Finch, and Alan C. Gange, "Green roof soil organisms: Anthropogenic assemblages or natural communities." Applied Soil Ecology, 2018; 126: 11 DOI: 10.1016/j.apsoil.2018.01.010.

19. Mia Taylor, "What a Green Roof Costs You on the Way to Saving Everything." The Street. May 22, 2015. Accessed June 8, 2018. https://www.thestreet.com/story/13161050/1/what-a-green-roof-costs-you-on-the-way-to-saving-everything.html.

20. Landscape Performance Series, "ASLA Headquarters Green Roof." January 23, 2015. Accessed June 9, 2018. https://landscapeperformance.org/case-study-briefs/asla-headquarters-green-roof.

21. C. Clark, P. Adriaens, and F. B. Talbot (2008). "Green roof valuation: a probabilistic economic analysis of environmental benefits," Environmental Science and Technology 42(6):2155–2161.

22. Graeme Hopkins and Christine Goodwin, *Living Architecture: Green Roofs and Walls* (Collingwood, Australia: CSIRO Publishing, 2011), Loc. 845 of 6129.

23. Rain Gardens and Bioswales | Soil Science Society of America. "Stormwater." Accessed June 9, 2018. https://www.soils.org/discover-soils/soils-in-the-city/green-roofs/stormwater.

24. ISDM, *Green Roofs and Living Walls for Architects* (North Charleston: CreateSpace, 2016), 10.

25. Sustainable Business, "Ford's green roof caps a decade of innovation." GreenBiz. November 22, 2013. Accessed June 10, 2018. https://www.greenbiz.com/blog/2013/11/22/fords-pioneering-green-roof-celebrates-10-years-sustainability.

26. "Greenroofs.com Projects—U.S. Postal Service (USPS) Morgan Processing and Distribution Center." SOLARIS at Fusionopolis (Phase 2B): From Military Base to Bioclimatic Eco-Architecture, By T. R. Hamzah & Yeang Sdn. Bhd. Accessed June 10, 2018. http://www.greenroofs.com/projects/pview.php?id=1070.

27. Queenie Wong, "Facebook's green roof mirrors company's workplace culture." Boulder Daily Camera. May 23, 2015. Accessed June 10, 2018. http://www.dailycamera.com/business/ci_28174708/menlo-park-facebooks-green-roof-mirrors-companys-workplace.

28. "Greenroofs.com Projects—Macy's Corporate Headquarters Habitat Roof." SOLARIS at Fusionopolis (Phase 2B): From Military Base to Bioclimatic Eco-Architecture, By T. R. Hamzah & Yeang Sdn. Bhd. Accessed June 10, 2018. http://www.greenroofs.com/projects/pview.php?id=1744.

29. Spencer Peterson, "Green-Roof Pioneering 'Groundscraper' to Seek a New Steward." Curbed. August 29, 2014. Accessed June 10, 2018. https://www.curbed.com/2014/8/29/10054420/weyerhaeuser-selling-corporate-headquarters.

30. Building Radar, "Green roofs—more than just a trend?" January 17, 2018. Accessed June 10, 2018. https://buildingradar.com/construction-blog/green-roofs/.

31. Korky Koroluk, "Construction Corner: New green roof design appears to be smart too." Constructconnect.com. Daily Commercial News. October 6, 2017. Accessed June 10, 2018. https://canada.constructconnect.com/dcn/news/technology/2017/10/construction-corner-new-green-roof-design-appears-to-be-smart-too-1027855w.

32. Paul Missios, Doug Banting, Hitesh Doshi, James Li, Angela Au, Beth Anne Currie, and Michael Verrati (2005). "Report on the Environmental Benefits and Costs of Green Roof Technology for the City of Toronto, III."

33. City of Toronto, "City of Toronto Green Roof Bylaw." December 10, 2017. Accessed June 10, 2018. https://www.toronto.ca/city-government/planning-development/official-plan-guidelines/green-roofs/green-roof-bylaw/.

34. Helen Ding, Sofia Faruqi, Andrew Wu, Juan-Carlos Altamirano, Andrés Anchondo Ortega, René Zamora Cristales, Robin Chazdon, Walter Vergara, and Michael Verdone, *Roots of Prosperity: The Economics and Finance of Restoring Land* (Washington, DC: World Resources Institute, 2017), 3.

35. The Biodiversity Consultancy, *Independent report on biodiversity offsets* (London: ICMM, 2013), 7.

36. National Fish and Wildlife Foundation, "Walmart and NFWF Announce Renewal of Acres for America Program for 10 Additional Years." Accessed June 10, 2018. http://www.nfwf.org/whoweare/mediacenter/pr/Pages/acres-10year_pr_15-1117.aspx.

37. International Finance Corporation, *Performance Standard 6: Biodiversity Conservation and Sustainable Management of Living Natural Resources* (Washington, DC: IFC, 2012), 2–3.

CHAPTER 4

Invasive Species: Profitable-Conservation Strategies

"It seems to me that the natural world is the greatest source of excitement; the greatest source of visual beauty; the greatest source of intellectual interest. It is the greatest source of so much in life that makes life worth living."
—David Attenborough

Invasive Species

You may be surprised to learn that invasive species rank second only to habitat destruction when it comes to the biggest threats to biodiversity.[1] In addition, the overall economic cost of invasive species in the United States is estimated to be around US$ 120 billion per year.[2] Despite the severity of the issue, I rarely see anything mentioned about invasive species when I read corporate sustainability reports. This doesn't necessarily mean that companies aren't doing anything to address the issue, but it does imply that invasive species aren't a top-of-mind environmental issue for companies and stakeholders. In this chapter, we'll learn the basics about invasive species and explore the different steps that corporations can take to combat the issue.

Let's start with some terminology, since there is quite a bit of confusion about the difference between terms like "biological invasion," "invasive," "native," "introduced," "endemic," and "indigenous." If definitions hurt your head, then feel free to skip the next five bulleted items!

- A "biological invasion" occurs when individuals of a species that aren't native to a region arrive with human assistance and spread in their new home.
- The term "invasive" refers to the behavior of spreading in the new region from the point of arrival.
- An "introduced" species arrives in an area with human help, but it includes species that don't establish populations or spread from the point of arrival. For example, if I plop some koi fish in your backyard pond, then you have an introduced species that has nowhere to go. If I drop 100 koi into a natural body of water, and they begin to multiply and spread throughout the waterway—wiping out native fish in the process—then the koi have become an invasive species. In other words, an introduced species doesn't become invasive unless the population spreads from the point of arrival.
- The term "native" refers to a place of origin rather than a behavior. So, a native species refers to a species that is living within its natural range.
- Native species come in two forms: endemic or indigenous. "Endemic" species are native species that are found only within one region. "Indigenous" species are native species that are found both within the region specified as well as in other regions. It's a subtle distinction for precise, science types.

If you've been paying close attention, you may have noticed that the terms "native" and "invasive" are technically not opposites, even though you'll commonly hear them used that way. You now know that "native" refers to a place of origin while "invasive" refers to the behavior of spreading from the point of arrival. For example, "native" and "nonnative" are opposites. Unfortunately, knowing these distinctions may not add much value to your life, and it probably won't even help you on *Jeopardy.* If all of this is gobbledygook, don't worry. You'll be able to get through the rest of the chapter without having to worry too much about the subtleties of definitions.

Invasive species may be brought into an area deliberately or accidentally, and many species of nonnative plants are deliberately brought in for horticultural use. For example, Kudzu (also known as "Japanese arrowroot") is a group of plants in the pea family that are native to parts of Asia and Pacific Islands. These climbing vines were first introduced into the United States for Philadelphia's 1876 Centennial Exposition. In the decades to follow, kudzu was identified as a possible solution to help prevent soil erosion. As a result, farmers sowed over a million acres of topsoil with kudzu. Big mistake! Kudzu became an invasive species, rapidly spreading from its point of arrival. Kudzu quickly climbed over native trees and shrubs, killing them by creating heavy shading. As a result, you can now find kudzu throughout the southeastern United States, particularly along roadsides and other disturbed areas.

Unlike the deliberate introduction of kudzu, many other invasive species arrive into a region by accident. One of the more infamous examples is the zebra mussel, which frequently appears on lists of the worst invasive species—and for good reason. It's estimated that zebra and quagga mussels cause US$ 1 billion per year in damages to water infrastructure and industries in the United States.[3]

Zebra mussels are native to the Caspian and Black Seas. Back in 1988, the zebra mussel hitched a ride in the ballast water of a transatlantic freighter, arriving in Lake St. Clair—a freshwater lake located between Ontario and Michigan. The mussel quickly spread to other watersheds, such as the Great Lakes and the Hudson River, by riding the currents and hitching a ride on anchors, the bottom of boats, and other human-mediated modes of transport.

Zebra mussels like to attach to stable objects. Stable objects can take the form of clams and other mussel species, which they can kill by reducing their ability to move, feed, and breed. This is how the zebra mussel wiped out certain species of clams in Lake St. Clair as well as other freshwater mussel species in Ireland. It's estimated that at least 30 species of freshwater mussel are threatened with extinction because of the zebra mussel.[4] Other stable objects to which zebra mussels like to attach include water-treatment-facility pipes and electricity-generation infrastructure. The mussels grow in thick densities, which can block pipes and clog water intakes. As a result, corporations in these industries spend a great deal of time and money removing mussels from their infrastructure.

Keep in mind that this is just one invasive species; there are a lot more out there. In 1999, one study estimated the existence of about 50,000 nonnative species in the United States, with about 4,300 of those considered invasive species.[5] More recent studies in the continental United States estimate that there are 6,000 to 7,000 introduced species of plants and animals, and roughly 10% to 20% of these introduced species are considered invasive.[6] In Hawaii, about half of the plants, 25% of the insects, most freshwater fish, and 40% of the birds are not native to the islands.[7] Putting all of this together, it's probably safe to say that we have about 1,000 invasive species in the United States today.

The impact of all of these introduced and invasive species on biodiversity can be severe. Invasive species can impact biodiversity by either altering the habitat so that some native species cannot survive or by targeting specific species through predation, disease, or hybridization. It's estimated that introduced species have played a role in endangering half of the imperiled species in the United States.[8] Introduced species pose a greater threat to biodiversity than the combined harm due to pollution, overharvesting, and disease.

A well-known predation example is the brown tree snake, which was carried on ships from islands near Papua New Guinea. Since its arrival in Guam, the brown-tree-snake population has exploded to an estimated 2 million snakes, with densities up to 13,000 per square mile in some places.[9] The result has not been good for local wildlife. The brown tree snake has eliminated 10 out of the 12 native bird species in local forests, including a species of kingfisher that can't be found anywhere else on Earth.[10] Today, the Guam kingfisher can only be found in captive breeding programs at zoos and other facilities.

Even the local trees are impacted by the snake. Some species of trees rely on birds to disperse seeds beyond the immediate vicinity of the parent tree. However, with the absence of birds, seed dispersal is not happening. Without birds, there's nothing else that can disperse seeds other than fruit bats, which are also nearly extinct on Guam.

From an economic perspective, the snakes have caused an estimated US$ 4.5 million in damage to electrical systems in Guam over the past seven years.[11] To combat the snake problem, the U.S. Department of Agriculture has created a US$ 8 million snake-eradication program that parachutes thousands of dead mice laced with toxic doses of paracetamol (also known as "acetaminophen"), which is toxic to brown snakes as well as to other animals.[12] The jury is still out on whether this program is a success.

Profitable-Conservation Strategies to Address Invasive Species

Now that we have a better understanding of the invasive-species issue, let's turn our focus to three basic strategies that corporations can take to help reduce the threat of invasive species: prevention processes, early detection and rapid response, and restoration of a native habitat.

Strategy #1: Prevention Processes

The best—and most cost-effective—way to manage invasive species is to keep out introduced species in the first place. Of course, that's easier said than done. To accomplish this, a company will need to implement a systematic process that targets common transportation pathways, such as ship ballast water, wooden packing material, and horticultural plants.

In some industries, the implementation of prevention processes for invasive species is required by law, such as ballast-water regulations to help prevent the introduction and spread of species like the zebra mussel. Financial lenders may also require precautionary measures. For example, International Finance Corporation Performance Standard 6 requires the company seeking a loan to "implement measures to avoid the potential for accidental or unintended introductions including the transportation of substrates and vectors (such as soil, ballast, and plant materials) that may harbor alien species."[13]

One effective approach that can be used by corporations is to implement a process like the Hazard Analysis and Critical Control Point (HACCP) process, which is used to reduce the risk of safety hazards in food. The HACCP process for food safety has been modified by the U.S. Fish and Wildlife Service to help prevent the spread of invasive species.

At a high level, the HACCP process includes seven basic steps:

1. **Conduct a hazard analysis.** The goal of a hazard analysis is to identify where species can be introduced. This includes the identification of risks as well as an estimate of the degree of risk.

2. **Identify critical control points.** Critical control points are the steps in your processes where controls can be applied to prevent the hitchhiking-species risks identified in your hazard analysis. You'll want to identify what types of preventive measures, such as washing vehicles, that you can take at these critical control points, focusing first on the high-risk hazards.

3. **Establish critical limits.** You'll define the criteria that must be met to control the hazard at each critical control point. In some cases, critical limits may already be specified by relevant regulations. For example, in 2013, the Environmental Protection Agency published a "Vessel General Permit," which includes specific prevention measures and limits to the maximum acceptable concentration of living

organisms per cubic meter of ballast water for commercial vessels 79 feet in length or greater.[14]

4. **Establish monitoring procedures.** Now that you've established specific critical limits, you'll need to specify what you'll measure, and how and when you'll measure it.
5. **Establish corrective actions.** You'll want to specify, in advance, the actions that you'll take if a critical limit is not met.
6. **Establish record-keeping procedures.** No process would be complete without documentation. Your process should include documentation demonstrating that critical limits have been met and the system is working as designed.
7. **Establish verification procedures.** As with any process, you'll want to periodically validate that your processes are working properly and are effective in preventing the hazards that you identified in Step #1. The results of these audits can be used to identify improvement opportunities for your overall HACCP process.

By implementing a formal process to monitor high-risk invaders at your company's critical control points, you can significantly reduce the risk of spreading introduced and invasive species on your property and throughout the local community.

Companies may also form partnerships to identify ways to prevent the spread of invasive species. A good example can be found in the shipping industry. A study estimated that 228 marine species are transported through ballast water or on the ship's exterior, and 57% of those species are considered harmful when introduced into nonnative ecosystems.[15] In response to this threat, four major shipping corporations (American President Lines, BP Shipping, Daewoo Shipbuilding & Marine Engineering, and Vela International Marine) have joined the International Maritime Organization, the United Nations Development Programme, and the Global Environment Facility to form the Global Industry Alliance. The Global Industry Alliance will share best practices on how to limit the number of invasive species transferred in ballast water and develop cost-effective, ballast-water treatment technologies. One of these technologies is the "ballast-free" ship (also known as "flow-through ballast tanks"). Ballast-free ships continuously run local seawater through a network of large pipes below the vessel's waterline rather than carry the same water between regions. This design could save about US$ 540,000 per ship, out of a total estimated cost of US$ 70 million, by saving the expense of building conventional filtration systems or ballast tanks.[16]

Strategy #2: Early Detection and Rapid Response

Prevention is our first line of defense; however, no matter how many regulations or how much money we throw at preventing invasive species, nonnative species will continue to arrive. When they do arrive, we'll want to have a second strategy in place to address this threat: early detection and rapid response (EDRR). For the "early detection" piece of EDRR, the goal is to have a monitoring program in place that will identify populations of nonnative species as early as possible before they have a chance to multiply and spread. The "rapid response" piece of EDRR is quite simple: We want to eradicate—or at least slow down—the invasive species after we spot it.

Early Detection

The earlier we detect an invasive species, the better chance we have at eradicating it in a manner that doesn't require heroic efforts, which translate into substantial costs and resources. One effective way is through the creation of a nationwide EDRR system.

The development of an EDRR system in the United States started in the early 1990s as state and federal agencies began to coordinate efforts to detect invaders. Since that time, a variety of EDRR databases has sprung up. Some databases focus on invasive plants while others have a very narrow focus. For example, the U.S. Forest Services has an EDRR database to help detect and monitor newly introduced exotic bark and ambrosia beetles at selected high-risk forest areas.

The landscape of EDRR efforts will no doubt change in the coming years, so I'll leave it to you to track down appropriate EDRR efforts in which you may want to participate. In the United States, a good place to start is the U.S. Department of the Interior as that agency is trying to create a national framework for EDRR. Similar efforts are underway in other parts of the world.

Corporations are encouraged to participate in EDRR efforts by enrolling their land in a sentinel-site program, which is an early-warning network that alerts scientists when invasive species are found in new regions. As part of this effort, a corporation would conduct a baseline inventory that can be included as part of the biodiversity assessment discussed in Chapter 3. The corporation then monitors its land to identify and report any changes to the baseline inventory of invasive species.

One of the biggest challenges that corporations face in participating in an EDRR system is finding staff who are trained to identify invasive species. Thankfully, that problem is relatively easy and inexpensive to solve. Simply contact your local university biology department or a local Native Plant Society, and you'll find many trained experts who are happy to help with your baseline inventory or ongoing monitoring. You may even be able to establish a partnership where the university gets access to your land to conduct research in exchange for monitoring the land for invasive species. For example, Royal Dutch Shell's Puget Sound Refinery awarded a US$ 10,000 grant to Northwest Straits Foundation to support efforts to monitor and eradicate local invasive species by the Skagit County Marine Resources Committee and its project partners.[17] The grant is being used to purchase equipment to monitor European green crabs.

European green crabs are an invasive species that is considered a threat to Puget Sound shellfish fisheries because it feeds on juvenile crabs, oysters, clams, and other shellfish, and it may compete with native fish and birds for food. The equipment will help "citizen scientists" monitor for green crabs in Padilla Bay and Fidalgo Bay near Shell's refinery and at other sites in adjacent counties.

The Skagit County Marine Resources Committee is partnering with a Crab Team that is sponsored by the University of Washington and the Washington Department of Fish & Wildlife. The Samish Indian Nation has also offered to help monitor and trap invasive green crabs. The monitoring and crab removals are managed by the Crab Team, with assistance from the Coastal Volunteer Partnership at Padilla Bay National Estuarine Research Reserve. This is a good example of the broad spectrum of stakeholders that can be leveraged to help monitor and manage invasive species.

Rapid Response

Once we've identified an invasive species, it's time to decide what to do next. In some cases, scientists will recommend that a newly introduced species be tolerated and monitored, as the cost of eradication may be too great, and some invasions will recede on their own. In other cases, it's time to act. This brings us to the "rapid response" portion of EDRR. Rapid response can come in the form of mechanical, chemical, or biological control.

"Mechanical control" refers to physically removing plants from the environment. This can be done through cutting, mowing, pulling, or suffocating plants by covering them with plastic sheeting. Mechanical control is highly effective, but it's also very labor-intensive, as anyone who has spent an afternoon weeding can tell you. Another thing to keep in mind is that mechanical control creates site disturbances that may lead to a rapid reinvasion if not managed properly. Finally, you'll need to give some thought to the best way of disposing the invasive species. Common methods include composting, drying, or burning the vegetation, either on-site or at the local landfill. Be sure to do these activities in a way that will prevent spreading the plants to other areas.

"Chemical control" uses herbicides to kill plants and prevent their return. Most of the common invasive-plant species in the United States can be treated by two herbicides: glyphosate and triclopyr. Glyphosate is a nonselective herbicide, which means that it kills everything it touches; triclopyr is a selective herbicide that does not harm monocots, such as grasses, orchids, and lilies. There are a variety of application techniques, such as cut-stem treatments and foliar applications, with which you'll want to become familiar to identify the best options for your site. Most companies will seek professional help to develop and implement a chemical-control program that is tailored for their site.

There are some pros and cons with using chemical control. On the positive side, herbicides are an effective and efficient way to manage invasive species. On the negative side, the improper use of herbicides can lead to health and environmental concerns. You may also need to obtain special permits to apply herbicides in wetlands or other areas, so you'll want to become familiar with your local pesticide regulations. Professional pesticide contractors will be able to help you navigate these options.

"Biological control" is the third method used to manage invasive species. Biological control uses insect predators or plant diseases to kill invasive species. The selected insect or plant disease is usually found in the home range of the target species. Biological control typically involves choosing one preferred insect predator or plant disease that is effective in targeting a single invasive species with minimal impact on nontarget species and the environment.

Biological control has proven to be one of the few effective tools for controlling widespread invasive plants. For example, several species of beetles were released to successfully control purple loosestrife (an invasive wetland plant) and St. John's wort (an invasive weed). However, this sort of tinkering requires careful thought and planning. It's easy to end up with unintended consequences.

For a real-life example, let's consider the gall fly and spotted knapweed. In the western United States, spotted knapweed—an invasive plant from Europe—has spread across millions of acres of hills and mountainsides. Gall flies were then imported to attempt to control spotted knapweed since the flies kill the weed in their native range. How does a fly kill a weed? Glad you asked! Gall flies lay eggs inside the seed head, which causes the plant to form a tumor-like growth called a "gall," which surrounds the eggs. Once the larvae emerge from the eggs, they eat the seeds of the plant. Problem solved, right? Not quite.

It turns out that deer mice really enjoy eating the fly larvae in the winter. After all, there isn't much other food around, and the gall fly larvae are already packaged up in a handy location above the snow. The mice climb the stalk of the spotted knapweed and eat the seed head. When other food sources are sparse, a deer mouse can eat as many as 1,200 larvae in a single night.[18] As a result, the population of deer mice has tripled.[19] Unfortunately, deer mice happen to be a carrier of hantavirus, a viral infection that's spread through mouse droppings and urine. Hantavirus can be fatal to humans, although it's quite rare. However, it provides a good example of the unintended consequences that can occur with a biological-control project.

Biological control can be an effective tool to combat invasive species, but it must be deployed carefully to minimize the risk of unintended consequences that we often don't fully understand until after the fact.

■ Strategy #3: Restoration of Native Habitat

The third strategy that corporations can take to combat the issue of invasive species is to restore a native habitat by removing introduced species and replacing them with native species. Restoring a native habitat may take the form of landscaping with native plants, planting meadows and gardens that are attractive to pollinators, and building wetlands or artificial ponds that provide water sources for local wildlife. For example, in Pacheco, Argentina, Volkswagen created an artificial lake near its facility to collect rainwater and provide a habitat for indigenous flora and fauna. This effort provides a natural landscape for the industrial center, and 62 species of birds have been counted at the lake.[20]

In this section, we'll focus on the topic of creating pollinator habitat, since around 80% of flowering plants rely on pollinators to some degree[21] and creating a native habitat for pollinators is something that companies of all sizes can easily do. Many homeowners can also pursue this strategy to support local plants and animals while improving the diversity and productivity of their land.

From a pollinator perspective, the best actions you can take involve protecting, enhancing, or restoring a wildflower-rich habitat that pollinators use for foraging. This action should include a variety of native plants that have overlapping blooming times to provide flowers for foraging throughout the seasons. You can also provide host plants for butterflies, nest sites for native bees, and undisturbed shelters for insect hibernation and overwintering.

It's also important to avoid using pesticides unless necessary. Pesticides have a negative impact on the pollinators that you're trying to attract. Corporations may want to consider implementing an integrated pest-management (IPM) strategy that utilizes a variety of chemical and nonchemical pest-control practices, which are only put in place once a pre-established pest-abundance threshold has been reached. In the United States, your local Cooperative Extension office can provide you with more information about integrated pest-management strategies that work well in your region. If you must use pesticides, it's important to use the minimum recommended dose, and apply the pesticides at times when pollinators are not active or when flowers are not present. For example, nighttime spraying, or spraying during periods of low temperature, have been shown to reduce bee mortality.

Many companies throughout the world have taken steps to plant native vegetation to protect biodiversity and attract native pollinators. For example, Daimler AG planted eight wildflower meadows, covering a total area of 48,000 square feet at its Mercedes-Benz plant in Bremen, Germany. The Bremen site also installed nest boxes for indigenous songbirds and swifts as well as an insect hotel for native species of bees, lacewings, and ladybugs.

If you want to learn more about attracting pollinators, the Xerces Society has published a variety of helpful resources, including a book called *Attracting Native Pollinators: Protecting North America's Bees and Butterflies.*

Return on Investment for Strategies to Combat Invasive Species

The return on investment (ROI) for removing invasive species and replacing them with native species will vary depending on the industry and the location of the business. In some cases, such as for ballast water, there will be regulatory drivers behind the action steps. For many companies, the value proposition for the restoration of a native habitat will come in the form of ecosystem services and more intangible benefits in the forms of employee satisfaction and fostering goodwill with customers, regulators, and the local community.

However, there are some cases where the proactive implementation of programs to prevent, detect, and respond to invasive species can yield more tangible cost savings. Let's take another look at the zebra mussel's impact on water-treatment and electricity-generating facilities.

In the United Kingdom, Thames Water spends £1 million a year on clearing zebra mussels from its raw water pipes and water-treatment facilities and applying heavy doses of chlorine to deter the mussels, while Anglian Water spends £500,000 a year tackling the problem.[22] In the United States, zebra mussels are estimated to have cost municipalities and power companies over US$ 1.5 billion over the past 25 years.[23] Another study came up with a lower cost estimate of US$ 267 million for all water-treatment and electricity-generating facilities from 1989 through 2004.[24] Whatever number you use, these are big numbers. Any prevention, early detection, and rapid-response actions that corporations in those industries successfully implement can yield a significant ROI.

Chapter 4 Action Steps

1. What introduced or invasive species do you have on your property? If you don't know, what steps can you take to find out?
2. What processes do you have in place to prevent and remove introduced and invasive species from your land? Would a modified HACCP process work well for your business? If so, what next steps will you take to design and implement the process?
3. What partnerships could you pursue that would help you develop cost-effective solutions to combat invasive species?
4. Do you landscape your property with native species, nonnative species, or both?
5. What actions can you take to restore native habitat and attract pollinators on your property?
6. How can you minimize the use of pesticides and herbicides on your property? Would an IPM strategy be appropriate for your business?

Chapter 4 Endnotes

1. Edward O. Wilson, *Half-Earth: Our Planet's Fight for Life* (New York: Liveright, 2017), 53.
2. The Nature Conservancy, "Impacts of Invasive Species." Red Foxes in Indiana | The Nature Conservancy. Accessed June 10, 2018. https://www.nature.org/ourinitiatives/urgentissues/land-conservation/forests/invasives-101.xml.
3. Catherine M. Thomas, "A cost-benefit analysis of preventative management for zebra and quagga mussels in the Colorado-Big Thompson System." Journal of Coastal Research. June 1, 2010. Accessed June 10, 2018. https://pubs.er.usgs.gov/publication/70118931.
4. Minnesota Sea Grant, "Zebra Mussels Threaten Inland Waters." Aquatic Invasive Species. Accessed June 10, 2018. http://www.seagrant.umn.edu/ais/zebramussels_threaten.
5. L. C. Corn, E. H. Buck, J. Rawson, and E. Fischer (1999). "Harmful Non-Native Species: Issues for Congress. Congressional Research Service Issue Brief, RL30123."
6. Daniel Simberloff, *Invasive Species: What Everyone Needs to Know* (Oxford: Oxford University Press, 2013), 27.
7. Ibid., 27-28.
8. Daniel Simberloff, "Introduced Species: The Threat to Biodiversity & What Can Be Done." ACTION BIOSCIENCE. December 2000. Accessed June 10, 2018. http://www.actionbioscience.org/biodiversity/simberloff.html.
9. Mike McRae, "Guam's Plague of Snakes Is Devastating The Whole Island Ecosystem, Even The Trees." ScienceAlert. March 11, 2017. Accessed June 10, 2018. https://www.sciencealert.com/guam-s-plague-of-snakes-is-having-a-devastating-impact-on-the-trees.
10. Ibid.
11. Ibid.
12. Ibid.
13. International Finance Corporation, *Performance Standard 6: Biodiversity Conservation and Sustainable Management of Living Natural Resources* (Washington, DC: IFC, 2012), 5.
14. U.S. Environmental Protection Agency, "Vessels—VGP." January 13, 2017. Accessed June 10, 2018. https://www.epa.gov/npdes/vessels-vgp.

15. Jennifer L. Molnar, Rebecca L Gamboa, Carmen Revenga, and Mark D Spalding, "Assessing the global threat of invasive species to marine biodiversity." Frontiers in Ecology and the Environment, November 1, 2008, 489.

16. Worldwatch Institute, "Alliance Formed to Limit Invasive Species." "Climate Change Will Worsen Hunger, Study Says." Accessed June 11, 2018. http://www.worldwatch.org/node/6035.

17. Northwest Straits Foundation Partners in Marine Conservation, "Northwest Straits Foundation awarded $10,000 grant from Shell Puget Sound Refinery in support for invasive species monitoring and eradication." Accessed June 11, 2018. http://nwstraitsfoundation.org/download/northwest-straits-foundation-awarded-10000-grant-from-shell-puget-sound-refinery-in-support-for-invasive-species-monitoring-and-eradication.

18. Jim Robbins, "A Weed, a Fly, a Mouse and a Chain of Unintended Consequences." The New York Times. April 4, 2006. Accessed June 12, 2018. https://www.nytimes.com/2006/04/04/science/04mice.html.

19. Ibid.

20. Volkswagen AG, "Argentina." Volkswagen Sustainability Report—CSR Projects—Brazil. Accessed June 12, 2017. https://csrprojects.volkswagenag.com/csr-projects/argentinien.html#0,1,2,3,4,5,6,7,8,9,10/8/0,1,2,3,4,5,6,7,8,9,10,11,12,13,14.

21. Food and Agriculture Organization of the United Nations, "Pollinators." Accessed June 12, 2018. http://www.fao.org/biodiversity/components/pollinators/en/.

22. WaterBriefing, "Water companies target zebra mussel infestation." August 5, 2011. Accessed June 12, 2018. https://www.waterbriefing.org/home/technology-focus/item/4490-water-companies-target-zebra-mussel-infestation.

23. Dan Egan, "The Great Takeover." September 7, 2017. Discover Magazine. Accessed June 12, 2018. http://discovermagazine.com/2017/oct/the-great-takeover.

24. N. A. Connelly, C. R. O'Neill, B. A. Knuth, et al., "Economic Impacts of Zebra Mussels on Drinking Water Treatment and Electric Power Generation Facilities." *Environmental Management* (2007) 40: 105. https://doi.org/10.1007/s00267-006-0296-5.

CHAPTER 5

Pollution, Climate Change, and Ocean Acidification: Profitable-Conservation Strategies

"Not all chemicals are bad. Without chemicals such as hydrogen and oxygen, for example, there would be no way to make water, a vital ingredient in beer."
—Dave Barry

Pollution, Climate Change, and Ocean Acidification

In this chapter, we'll tackle three threats to wildlife and biodiversity: pollution, climate change, and ocean acidification. Rather than regurgitate large amounts of information with which you're probably already familiar, I've lumped these three topics into a relatively short chapter, with an emphasis on how these issues relate to biodiversity and wildlife conservation and the role that corporations can play to address these challenges.

Pollution

"Pollution" refers to the introduction of contaminants, such as chemicals, light, noise, or heat, into the natural environment where they may cause negative changes. Fortunately, this is one threat to biodiversity and wildlife that corporations of all shapes and sizes are willing to address, at least to some degree. This is largely due to the thousands of pages of environmental regulations with which corporations must comply to ensure that processes and controls are in place for air emissions, wastewater and stormwater discharge, and hazardous-material transport and storage.

However, regulatory pressure isn't the only reason why corporations pay close attention to pollution. Many of the actions that corporations take to prevent pollution also produce significant cost savings. In addition, the approach that corporations need to take to address pollution include processes and ways of thinking that are familiar to them. When you talk about "minimizing waste" and "improving process efficiency," you're speaking the language of business. Waste minimization and process efficiency are topics that already get a lot of attention in corporations through a variety of initiatives, such as Lean, Six Sigma, and quality-management systems.

Pollution ranks third on the list of threats to biodiversity and wildlife.[1] The release of chemicals in an ecosystem can have a wide range of negative impacts to wildlife, plants, and human health. For example, herbicides and pesticides cause harm to nontarget species, such as insect pollinators, and pose a risk to human health. Coal-burning power plants and chlorine production plants generate heavy metals that can make their way into soils and watersheds. This can lead to high levels of heavy metals, such as mercury, in many species of fish. Mercury and other heavy metals are dangerous to ecosystems and to human health.

The discharge of detergents, fertilizers, and sewage into aquatic systems can cause an excess of nutrients, such as nitrogen and phosphorus, which disrupt ecosystems by causing the overgrowth and decay of plants, algae, and phytoplankton. The result is a severe decline in water quality and the creation of an aquatic environment that promotes the survival of simple algae and plankton over more complicated plants. The fancy term for this scenario is "eutrophication." You may also hear about "algal blooms," which refer to a scenario in aquatic habitats where we see a significant increase in phytoplankton in response to higher levels of phosphates and other nutrients.

Then we have the example of acid rain. The burning of fossil fuels generates air pollutants that can either remain in the air as particle pollutants or fall to the ground in the form of acid rain. The sulfuric- and nitric-acid components of acid rain can lead to the acidification of lakes, streams, and forest soils. Species of fish, amphibians, clams, snails, insects, and plants can have a difficult time surviving in acidic conditions. Fish eggs can't hatch if the pH of water is too low, and fish species, such as salmon, may abandon their spawning areas. When fewer fish spawn and fewer eggs hatch, it creates fewer food options for predators. Acid rain also harms plants and trees by slowing their growth, damaging their leaves, and making the soil more toxic to plants. The key point is that pollution, in all its forms, can cause serious, widespread harm to wildlife and the ecosystems upon which they depend.

Climate Change

Let's turn our attention to a special form of pollution: the release of carbon dioxide into the environment. In other words, it's time to look at the hot-button topic of climate change.

Like politics and religion, climate change is one of those polarizing subjects that can really enrage folks. One camp will argue that climate change is a real phenomenon largely created by human activities. Another camp believes that climate change can be attributed to natural temperature fluctuations over which humans have little control. Then we have a third camp of climate-change agnostics who aren't sure.

Rest assured that I won't be launching into a climate-change debate here. The data to support climate change seem very compelling, but I'm not a climate scientist, and climate change isn't my area of expertise. However, no matter what side of the debate you embrace, many surveys show that most of the public, and most scientists, believe that climate change is real and is caused by human activities.

As the saying goes, perception is reality, or at least it plays a major role in how we model reality. Climate change is not a topic that corporations can ignore, particularly in industries that burn substantial amounts of fossil fuel, such as the oil and gas, automotive, and utilities industries. Since climate change is such an important issue for business, biodiversity, and wildlife, let's start with a short primer on the topic.

As you probably know, the Earth's climate has been changing constantly over geological time, and New Mexico, where I live, is a good example. Parts of New Mexico were once submerged by a warm, shallow sea; today, I need to catch a two-hour flight to get to the nearest ocean.

On planet Earth, we've had periods with average temperatures higher and lower than the 59-degree F (or 15-degree C) average that we see today. However, scientists believe that the current period of warming is happening at a faster rate than it has in the past, and the reason for this relatively rapid increase can be attributed to human activities.

More specifically, gases released from industry and agriculture are thought to be the culprit. The biggest human-caused sources of these "greenhouse gases"—particularly carbon dioxide—are a result of burning fossil fuels and cutting down carbon-absorbing forests. Greenhouse gases got that name because they prevent heat from escaping the Earth's surface. Since heat can't escape the Earth's surface, we see an increase in the Earth's surface temperature.

Increases in temperature can have a massive impact on biodiversity and wildlife. Some habitats may disappear due to rising sea levels, which are caused by the melting of mountain glaciers and polar ice sheets. Temperature changes have an impact on flowering and fruiting times for plants. They also have a significant impact on the habitat ranges that are occupied by animals. Biologists on the ground are witnessing significant shifts in habitat ranges and species composition in different parts of the world. Some species are showing up in areas where they haven't been seen previously while other species are starting to disappear from areas where they were once abundant. I recently went to a presentation that showed slide after slide of striking shifts in locations where New Mexico birds have been spotted in the state over the past few decades.

For species that can survive in a wide variety of habitat patches, climate change may not pose a major threat. However, species that are isolated in just a few habitat patches or are restricted to mountaintops may not be able to rapidly shift their distribution to survive. There are synergies between habitat loss, habitat fragmentation, and climate change that can compound the effects of habitat destruction on biodiversity and wildlife. Wildlife corridors or habitat linkages may provide an important piece of the puzzle to enable species to move to a suitable habitat as conditions change.

Ocean Acidification

Ocean acidification doesn't get nearly as much attention as climate change, but it's an important topic nonetheless. In fact, ocean acidification and climate change are relatives. Here's how they're related.

Remember all the carbon dioxide that gets emitted into the air and causes climate change? Well, the same carbon dioxide that's emitted into the air eventually ends up in our oceans. When carbon dioxide gets absorbed into our oceans, it makes the water more acidic and reduces the amount of calcium-carbonate minerals. Both scenarios are bad for aquatic life.

Let's start with calcium carbonate. Many aquatic animals require calcium-carbonate minerals to survive. That's because calcium-carbonate minerals are the building blocks for the protective shells and skeletons that coral, crabs, plankton, sea urchins, sea stars, and other animals need for protection.

The acidic environment, on the other hand, has a negative impact on fish populations. The acidic environment can cause changes in the blood chemistry of fish, which leads to changes in the behavior and health in some species. It's estimated that ocean water has become 30% more acidic over the past 200 years, which is faster than any known change in ocean chemistry over the past 50 million years.[2]

When populations of some of these animal species decrease, it decreases the amount of food available for species higher on the food chain that feed on them. In other words, carbon dioxide that is absorbed into the ocean can cause a chain reaction that impacts an entire marine ecosystem.

Profitable-Conservation Strategies for Pollution, Climate Change, and Ocean Acidification

Now that we have that glum news out of the way, let's look at some strategies that corporations can use to address the threats of pollution, climate change, and ocean acidification. We'll discuss five common approaches: pollution prevention, environmental design, green building, green infrastructure, and carbon-offset programs.

■ Strategy #1: Pollution Prevention

Most corporations have a pollution-prevention program or project in place. These efforts are usually based on the well-known "reduce, reuse, and recycle" concept. Many of these pollution-prevention efforts are regulatory driven, following specific guidance from various regulatory agencies. Other pollution-prevention initiatives aim to go beyond compliance, driven by a company's desire to identify cost-saving opportunities that also reduce pollution. No matter what the driver, there are seven basic steps that a company follows when implementing a pollution-prevention initiative.

◆ Step #1: Create pollution-prevention goals.

A good place for any company to start is to first reach agreement on the overall purpose and goals for initiating a pollution-prevention program. These goals usually include voluntary targets for reducing the amount of pollution via air, water, or waste along with targets for cost savings. Some goals are ambitious, such as zero waste by 2020; other goals may be modest, such as a 1% reduction from current levels of pollution by 2020. The quantitative goals and financial targets that you select will come in handy in Step #2.

You'll also want to specify if your pollution-prevention initiative will be set up in the form of a program or a project. A project has a defined scope with a definite start and end date. A program has no end date and may include a series of projects that, taken together, will accomplish a set of objectives. A program will use common standards and processes for the portfolio of projects that it contains. There are more subtleties in comparing a project to a program, but this distinction is good enough for our purposes.

◆ Step #2: Obtain commitment from senior management.

In this step, it's time to sell your concept to senior managers at your company. To do this, you'll need to present a solid business case to justify why the company should invest time, money, and resources on your proposed pollution-prevention effort. Thankfully, it's relatively easy to set tangible, quantitative goals for pollution-prevention efforts. To be successful, you'll want to present data that show how your proposal is aligned with the organization's mission and strategic plan, and how it will yield a solid return on investment (ROI) for the organization. Commitment from senior management is a critical step in ensuring that your pollution-prevention initiative will be a success.

◆ Step #3: Create a pollution-prevention team.

Congratulations! Your senior-management team approved your proposal! Now it's time to form a team that will help you accomplish those great things to which you committed in your proposal to senior management. The effort may be facilitated by a member of your environmental team, but you'll likely want to pull in subject-matter experts from a wide variety of areas. Your team should include a variety of job functions that will provide different perspectives on how to approach the effort from financial, legal, technical, and operations perspectives. Different teammates may be pulled in at different phases of the effort.

◆ Step #4: Collect baseline data.

To determine if your pollution-prevention efforts are a success, you'll first need to collect baseline data for the pollutants and processes that are in scope. This baseline data may include a variety of cost, emissions, and process-efficiency data.

◆ Step #5: Identify, prioritize, and select pollution-prevention opportunities to implement.

In this step, the team lead will facilitate sessions with subject-matter experts to create a list of possible approaches that the organization may wish to take. Once you have an exhaustive list, you'll go through a prioritization exercise to identify the best option(s) to pursue. To do this, you'll probably want to use a scorecard that assigns different weights to various factors, such as the environmental effectiveness or impact, ease of implementation, costs, benefits, and ROI for each approach. Your baseline data from Step #4 will come in handy for this exercise.

◆ Step #6: Implement pollution-prevention initiatives.

At this point, you know what pollution-prevention activity or activities you will pursue. Now it's time for implementation. This can be done as a pilot test for one part of your operation or as a full-scale implementation throughout the organization.

◆ Step #7: Conduct a post-implementation review.

After you've implemented your pollution-prevention initiatives for the prespecified time, the next step is to determine if your efforts were a success. To do this, you'll need to do another round of data collection, using the same methodology used to collect the baseline data. Once you've collected the data and crunched the numbers, you can identify which efforts to continue, which efforts to adjust, and which efforts to scrap and replace with the next highest priority initiatives from the list you generated in Step #5. If the initiative was set up as a project, then you'll close the project, transition it to operations, and open new projects as needed. If this was part of a larger program, then you'll keep rolling, capture lessons learned, and adjust your overall project portfolio as needed.

Profitable Pollution-Prevention Efforts for Business and the Environment

Pollution-prevention activities that yield the biggest value for business and the environment will vary, depending on the company, industry, and location. Here are some examples to help you get your creative juices flowing:

- **Training programs.** One tried-and-true approach with successful outcomes in any industry is to conduct formal training sessions to help facilities around the world identify and implement pollution-prevention activities that have proven to be successful in other sites, companies, or industries. For example, when I worked as an Environmental Programs Manager at Coca-Cola, we had an internal training program called "Waste$mart," which helped bottling and concentrate facilities around the world identify and implement cost-saving opportunities and reduce the amount of pollution and waste that the facilities generated. Each training session typically yielded hundreds of thousands of dollars in potential energy-saving strategies for each bottling plant and concentrate facility.[3]

- **Energy audits.** An "energy audit" (also known as an "energy assessment") is an evaluation of a building's energy systems to look for opportunities to reduce energy use. Since a typical commercial building wastes about 30% of the energy used to run it,[4] energy audits can be an excellent way to save money and reduce pollution. The best areas on which to focus are usually heating, ventilation, and air conditioning (HVAC) systems as well as lighting systems. By changing the type of light fixture, reducing the number of light fixtures to "right-light" a space, and adding controls, some buildings have been able to reduce energy use by as much as 80% to 90%, while maintaining or even improving overall lighting quality.[5] Energy audits can also help companies determine if renewable energy sources, such as solar and wind, are a good avenue for the company to pursue.
- **Printers and paper.** One of the easiest and quickest wins for companies is to look for opportunities to switch from paper-based systems to electronic systems. The health-care industry is a good example. I've worked with medical providers and medical-insurance companies where I've seen a large push in recent years to move away from paper files and documents and replace them with electronic medical records and forms, which patients can complete online at home or on-site via kiosks or tablets in waiting rooms. Some of these efforts were driven from government incentives, such as Meaningful Use, but other efforts were driven primarily from a desire to save money.

  When it comes to printers, another popular option is to adjust the default printer settings to double-sided. It doesn't get much easier than that! Yet, a company with 5,000 employees that chooses to make this printer-setting adjustment for only 10% of its printing can save as much as US$ 260,000 per year.[6]

  While we're on the topic of printers, you may want to consider reducing the number of standalone printers in your company. Granted, this might not make you popular with some people, but the cost savings can be significant. I managed a printer-reduction / printer-upgrade project for a health-care provider with about 1,000 employees, and I was surprised to learn that many of the standalone printers had utilization rates hovering around 1% to 2%, yet they continued to draw power around the clock.

Another money-saving action is to require employees to enter a personal identification number or swipe their badge to collect a print job; otherwise, the print job gets canceled after a certain time. Once again, this may not make you the most popular person in the building, but the cost savings from changes like these can really add up. One study estimated that simple measures to reduce paper can save up to US$ 1,250 per employee per year, with an ROI of 300%.[7] There's plenty of low-hanging fruit when it comes to printers and paper in many organizations.

- **Information technology (IT).** There are a variety of "green computing" or "green IT" practices that can help you improve energy efficiency, reduce the use of hazardous materials, improve product longevity, and promote the biodegradability of products that are no longer needed. For most companies, the best opportunities come in the form of improving energy efficiency of data centers and adjusting power-management settings on individual computers.

  For example, by automatically putting idle computers into a low-power sleep mode, organizations may save up to US$ 50 per computer each year.[8] The University of Wisconsin at Oshkosh implemented this power-management strategy for its 2,900 faculty, staff, and student lab computers, which saved US$ 76,500 each year.[9] Over the three-year useful life of a typical computer, that added up to a cost savings of over US$ 200,000.[10] At the same time, this action prevented more than 3,520 tons of carbon dioxide ($CO_{2)}$ emissions,[11] which is the same amount of CO_2 that is absorbed naturally by 725 acres worth of trees.[12] The Environmental Protection Agency estimates that 70% to 80% of U.S.-based organizations haven't pursued this simple power-management option.[13]

- **Food and beverage waste.** There are a wide variety of ways that companies can reduce the impacts associated with its cafeterias. Companies like Genentech have eliminated foam cups and containers and encourage employees to bring their own coffee mugs and water bottles. In the cafeterias of places like Genentech and Whole Foods, you'll find separate bins for recycling, compost, and landfill, with visual displays that make it easy for people to identify which bins to use. These companies are also vigilant about choosing sustainable menu options that are healthy, seasonal, and locally sourced. Given the variety of healthy options at the Genentech cafeteria, employees considered the cafeterias to be one of the perks of working at Genentech.

- **Packaging.** The reduction of unnecessary packaging can be a significant win-win strategy that is good for the environment and good for the bottom line. For example, Walmart created a tool for apparel buyers and sourcing teams to help them optimize the size of corrugated cardboard shipping cartons. As a result, Walmart was able to reduce the number of boxes shipped by 8.1 million in one year, saving 6.3 million pounds of corrugate, 7,800 metric tons of greenhouse gases, and US$ 15.3 million in operational costs.[14] In some cases, Walmart was able to eliminate packaging completely. The company now uses hangers instead of boxes for 85 million pairs of shoes. These space utilization improvements reduced costs by US$ 9 million, while saving another 16 million pounds of corrugate and preventing the release of over 20,000 metric tons of greenhouse gases.[15]
- **Transportation and fleet efficiency.** Transportation and fleet opportunities include creating incentives for employees who take public transportation or company shuttles to the office, reducing business travel with the use of videoconferences, selecting fuel-efficient trucks for transportation of products, and calculating ideal routes to maximize fuel efficiency. Walmart implemented "effective driving techniques" (minimizing idle time and progressive shifting), "advanced tractor-trailer technologies" (electrification, light-weighting, advanced control systems, improved aerodynamics, and fuel-efficient tires), and "improved processes and systems to drive efficient loading and routing of merchandise" for its roughly 6,000 trucks. Through these efforts, Walmart was able to double fleet efficiency over the course of 10 years, which eliminated 650,000 metric tons of greenhouse gases and saved the company nearly US$ 1 billion.[16]
- **Green teams.** Green teams are self-organized, cross-functional groups of employees who voluntarily come together to help their organization identify and implement a variety of environmental initiatives. These grassroots efforts are a great way to keep employees informed

and engaged and the company accountable for improving its environmental performance.

Green teams have been successfully implemented in a wide variety of companies and industries, such as Advanced Micro Devices, Hyatt, Citibank, eBay, DaVita, and Genentech. At Genentech, the green team is called Green Genes, and it's now the company's largest employee club with over 4,000 employee members.[17] Green Genes hosts a variety of environmental activities—everything from Lunch and Learns programs and movies on environmental topics to Eco Fairs and beach cleanups. Green Genes has also helped drive changes at Genentech, such as expanding programs for on-site water conservation, energy conservation, and composting as well as leading a variety of landfill-reduction and food-waste minimization initiatives.

- **Research and innovation.** Many companies partner with universities and nongovernmental organizations to conduct research on cost-effective strategies to address climate change and other environmental challenges. For example, in Italy, Lamborghini launched a project called "Lamborghini for biodiversity—Oak Forest Research Project." With Lamborghini's home municipality of Sant'Agata Bolognese and the universities of Bologna, Bolzano, and Munich, this project involves planting 10,000 oak seedlings and conducting research studies to analyze the relationships between vegetation, climate, and CO_2.[18]

The list of profitable pollution-prevention activities goes on and on. Pollution prevention is a strategy that every corporation should actively pursue as it yields so many win-win opportunities for business, biodiversity, and wildlife.

Strategy #2: Environmental Design

A second powerful corporate strategy for addressing pollution, climate change, and ocean acidification is to design products, processes, or services in a way that reduces impacts to human health and the environment. This approach is called Design for the Environment (DfE), and the concept has been around since the early 1990s. In 1992, the Environmental Protection Agency got on board with the idea by creating a DfE program, which it later rebranded as "Safer Choice" in 2015.

DfE looks at a process from start to finish, including everything from raw-material extraction and processing to manufacturing, packaging, and disposal. To do this, companies often use an approach called life-cycle assessment (LCA) to compare the cradle-to-grave impacts of a specific product with the impacts of modified versions of the product. This is data-intensive work, and companies use a variety of software tools and databases to evaluate product impacts, such as toxicity, energy use, acidification, ozone depletion, CO_2 emissions, and resource depletion.

DfE is more commonly found in industries that use a lot of chemical ingredients in their products or processes, such as the electronics industry. Companies like IBM, Hewlett-Packard (HP), and Philips use DfE to identify chemical alternatives that are better for the environment without sacrificing product quality or performance. These companies also look for ways to make it safer and easier to reuse or dispose of products at the end of a product's useful life. This is partly driven by "product take-back" and "extended producer responsibility" (EPR) regulations and pressures for companies to accept used products, such as electronics, batteries, mercury thermometers, carpets, pharmaceuticals, pesticide containers, cell phones, fluorescent lighting, and paint. Product take-back and EPR regulations are common in Europe and Japan, and many U.S. states have also passed EPR legislation, particularly for the recycling of electronic waste.

Profitability of DfE as a Conservation Strategy

By going through a DfE process, companies can identify a variety of alternative materials and processes that can lead to significant cost reductions while decreasing their contribution to pollution, climate change, and ocean acidification. DfE is also used as a risk-management strategy that helps organizations meet environmental regulations and improve relations with regulatory agencies, consumers, and the local community.

In some cases, DfE initiatives may bring new business and market opportunities to light. For example, HP's DfE program identified an opportunity to use recycled plastic instead of virgin plastic for its ink cartridges. Through collaboration with recycling and materials suppliers, more than 80% of HP ink cartridges and 100% of HP LaserJet toner cartridges now contain recycled plastics. This has enabled HP to reduce greenhouse-gas emissions by 43 million pounds from 2013 to 2015,[19] which is equivalent to taking 4,125 cars off the road for one year.[20] Through these types of design and technical innovations, HP is well on its way to achieving its goal to reduce product-portfolio, greenhouse-gas emissions by 25% from 2010 to 2020.[21]

■ Strategy #3: Green Building

Green building is a well-known, cost-effective, environmental-management strategy that businesses have adopted with enormous success. "Green building" has a variety of definitions, but it generally refers to the planning, design, construction, and operation of buildings in a way that minimizes the overall impact on the environment. In discussions about green building, somebody will inevitably mention the Leadership in Energy and Environmental Design (LEED) rating system. LEED is a globally recognized framework and rating system that is used to create efficient, healthy, and cost-saving green buildings.

Through the LEED program, buildings that meet certain criteria are rated with certification levels of Certified, Silver, Gold, or Platinum. The different ratings are based on a scoring system that looks at six key areas: sustainable sites, water efficiency, energy and atmosphere, materials and resources, indoor environmental quality, and innovation in design.

LEED has helped create a green-building industry that is valued at approximately US$ 250 billion in the United States alone.[22] There are currently more than 60,000 commercial projects worldwide that participate in LEED.[23] The U.S. Green Building Council estimates that commercial building owners and managers will invest US$ 960 billion globally between 2015 and 2023 on greening their existing buildings.[24] The primary areas of focus are expected to include the installation of more energy-efficient HVAC systems, windows, lighting, and plumbing fixtures.

Profitability of Green Building as a Conservation Strategy

There's a good reason why green building is so popular. Green building reduces environmental impacts and provides a substantial ROI.

The value proposition of green building and LEED certification to corporations comes in many forms. For starters, LEED-certified buildings have lower operating costs. Green building owners report an ROI of 19.2% on average for existing building projects and 9.9% on average for new projects.[25] One study estimated that the average annual utilities cost per employee in green buildings was US$ 675.26 lower than in nongreen facilities, and LEED-certified buildings used 25% less energy and lowered operational costs by 19%.[26] Corporations can also get a variety of tax benefits and incentives, such as expedited building permits, fee waivers, or fee reductions from local regulatory agencies.

One comprehensive 2012 U.S. Green Building Council study found that LEED office buildings in Wa shington, DC, used 13% less energy per square foot, 11% lower average electricity usage, and 16% lower average water usage compared to non-LEED-certified office buildings.[27]

Green buildings are also linked to significant improvements in health and productivity for the people working there. One U.S. Department of Energy study found that green-building retrofits reduced communicable respiratory diseases by 9% to 20%, reduced allergies and asthma by 18% to 25%, and reduced nonspecific health and discomfort effects by 20% to 50%.[28] Green buildings also create happier employees, positive publicity, and favorable perceptions from customers and the local community.

Software maker Adobe Systems has embraced green building with 22 LEED certifications for its buildings, including 8 Platinum certifications.[29] The com-pany now has more than 2.9 million square feet of LEED-certified space, which represents 76% of Adobe Systems workspaces.[30] Adobe's green-building invest-ments have clearly paid off. In 2006, Adobe estimated a net-present-value rate of return of nearly 20:1 for the initial investment in its headquarters towers.[31]

In short, green building is a profitable-conservation strategy on steroids!

■ Strategy #4: Green Infrastructure

Green infrastructure is like green building, but it can take some different forms than a building or roof. The term "green infrastructure" is defined differently by various organizations, but it generally refers to natural systems that are managed to address urban challenges, such as stormwater management, climate adaptation, clean water, and healthy soils. "Gray infrastructure" refers to any man-made solutions that typically involve concrete and steel. You'll also hear the term "hybrid infrastructure," which utilizes a combination of green and gray infrastructure to provide an optimal solution to a challenge. Let's look at an example to better illustrate what the heck we're talking about.

Union Carbide Corporation, a subsidiary of The Dow Chemical Company, constructed a 110-acre wetland in Texas to serve the function of a wastewater-treatment facility. The original water-treatment system included various treatment ponds, including a 267-acre tertiary pond, but the facility was exceeding its discharge-permit criteria for total suspended solids, and it required extensive, daily pH adjustments. Union Carbide explored several options and, after a conducting a one-year pilot test, decided to convert part of its tertiary pond into a constructed wetland. The wetland took 18 months and an initial investment of US$ 1.4 million before it was fully operational.[32]

There were several pros and cons associated with the project, which has now been in operation for 15 years. From a risk standpoint, the wetland creates the potential need to comply with new regulations, such as coliform bacteria. In addition, disturbances from wildlife, such as nutria, alligators, and bobcats, needed to be managed. There was also a risk that a threatened or endangered species would be found in the wetland, which could impact operations. However, the facility determined that this was a minimal risk since none of the 46 threatened or endangered species near the site would be expected to occupy the wetland habitat.

In terms of benefits, the wetland was 100% compliant from day zero with all discharge requirements for total suspended solids, and it has eliminated the need to adjust discharge pH. The project also has low-energy, maintenance, and resource requirements with no need for pumps, additives, an oxygen system, or added water, and there are no biosolids to handle or dispose. From a cost perspective, the US$ 1.4 million initial investment and operational capital pales in comparison to the US$ 40 million price tag for a gray infrastructure alternative. Of course, the local wildlife benefit from the wetland, and the amount of biodiversity is much greater in the constructed wetland compared with a conventional wastewater-treatment plant. It's a good example of a win-win, profitable-conservation project.

Similar types of green-infrastructure projects have been implemented to mitigate air pollution through reforestation (The Dow Chemical Company and The Nature Conservancy), provide erosion control for pipelines using constructed oyster reefs and natural vegetation (Shell Oil Company and The Nature Conservancy), and water treatment through forest- and land-management practices and watershed conservation (The Nature Conservancy and the Cauca Valley Water Fund in the Cali region of Colombia).

Strategy #5: Carbon-Offset Programs

"Carbon offsets" (also known as "greenhouse-gas offsets") are a popular tool that corporations use to address climate change. Carbon-offset programs are set up to reduce emissions of carbon dioxide or other greenhouse gases in a certain area to compensate for emissions that are made elsewhere. Carbon offsets are particularly popular in Europe, with about 80% of the carbon-market volume and 77% of the carbon-market value.[33] North America has roughly 17% of the carbon-market volume and 22% of the value, while China has 1% and 0.3%, respectively.[34]

Carbon offsets are purchased in units of one ton of CO_2e that has not been emitted into the atmosphere. Offsets may come in the form of a variety of initiatives to reduce carbon emissions, such as planting trees to absorb CO_2 from the air or by switching to fuel sources that have a smaller carbon footprint. Many corporations are attracted to carbon offsets because they are often a cheaper way to stay in compliance when compared with the steps required to further reduce emissions. As a result, corporations are usually limited in the quantity of offsets that they can purchase.

There are two types of markets in which corporations can participate: compliance markets and voluntary markets.

In compliance markets, corporations, governments, and other organizations purchase carbon offsets to meet regulatory caps on the total amount of greenhouse gases they are permitted to emit. Government agencies set the rules that govern the types of offsets permitted in compliance markets as well as the methods for demonstrating compliance.

The second, much smaller market is the voluntary market. In a voluntary market, corporations, governments, or individuals can purchase carbon offsets to mitigate their greenhouse-gas emissions from electricity use and transportation, such as air travel. Some companies give customers the option to buy carbon offsets as an upsell during the sale of a product or service. For example, the airline industry introduced this as an option, but only about 1% to 3% of passengers purchased the offset.[35] In contrast to the compliance market, the rules that govern a voluntary market are set by voluntary standard bodies. In 2016, approximately US$ 191.3 million and 63.4 million tons of carbon-dioxide equivalent were bought and sold in the voluntary market, which is a 24% drop compared with 2015 data.[36]

Another important distinction between compliance markets and voluntary markets is price. In a compliance market, the price of 1 ton of carbon dioxide is roughly the same everywhere. The reduction of 1 ton of CO_2 in one place is viewed as having the same effect as reducing 1 ton of CO_2 in another location.

In voluntary markets, you'll find a huge amount of price variation, depending on the project location, project type, and standard that is being followed. For example, wind offsets from Asia were traded at an average of US$ 0.7 per ton of CO_2e, afforestation and reforestation offsets from Africa were traded at an average of US$ 6.7 per ton of CO_2e, and other types of offsets were traded as high as US$ 50 per ton of CO_2e.[37] These prices reflect the fact that a corporation may pay significantly more for an offset that comes from a project located near its operations or for an offset that has been verified under a certain standard.

This variation in pricing and other characteristics of carbon-offset projects have led to some criticism about the use of "good-quality" versus "bad-quality" offsets. Critics view carbon offsets simply as a tool that enables corporations to avoid reducing emissions. Others argue that carbon offsets give corporations credit for greenhouse-gas reductions that would have occurred without the offset program. Sometimes these criticisms are valid, and sometimes they're not. It depends on the situation and the company.

There's a lot more to the world of carbon-offset programs, but hopefully this gives you a rough idea of the concept. I encourage you to learn more about the pros and cons of carbon-offset programs if this is an area of interest. You'll also want to dive into the details of the specific carbon-offset programs that are available to your organization based on your location and regulatory requirements.

Profitability of Carbon-Offset Programs as a Conservation Strategy

Carbon offsets enable many companies to meet regulatory requirements at a significantly lower cost compared with the effort and resources required to directly reduce emissions from operations. The actual ROI will depend on your specific situation. You'll need to compare your costs to install additional pollution-prevention infrastructure and processes with the cost of purchasing carbon offsets that are available to your company.

As for the benefits to wildlife and biodiversity, the jury is still out. However, a recent Stanford University study provides some positive news on the biodiversity front. The study focused on a forest-offset program in California, which allows forest owners around the United States to sell carbon credits to California companies that are required reduce emissions. Under this program, forest owners earn a credit of about US$ 10 for each additional ton of carbon dioxide that their trees store. They can then sell this credit to help California companies offset their greenhouse-gas emissions.[38] The results have been positive. The forest-offset program has created an incentive for forest owners to change their forest-management practices so that their trees will store more carbon. For example, the forest owners cut trees less often and restored previously forested land. This can be a good thing for wildlife and biodiversity, as 17 of the 39 forest-offset projects that were analyzed included habitat for endangered species.

Of course, there are other factors that need to be considered when it comes to evaluating the impact to biodiversity and wildlife. Tree plantations often consist of dense stands of trees that are planted in rows, composed of trees that are the same age and species. These monoculture stands of trees are not associated with high levels of biodiversity. In addition, tree plantations may use chemical fertilizers and herbicides, which can impact native species. High tree densities may use substantial amounts of water and increase the risk of fire. Finally, the amount of carbon dioxide that a tree will absorb will depend on the species of tree and factors like soil type and below-ground biomass.

Despite these possible concerns, the Stanford study does give us some reasons to be optimistic. So far, forest owners have earned roughly US$ 250 million since the program began in 2013.[39] At the same time, 25 million tons of carbon have been offset, which is equivalent to 5% of California's annual passenger vehicle emissions.[40] These results are encouraging, and the hope is that other states and countries will be inspired to develop forest-offset programs that are designed to benefit corporations, wildlife, and biodiversity.

Chapter 5 Action Steps

1. Describe the impacts that your company has on pollution, climate change, and ocean acidification.
2. What pollution-prevention programs do you currently have in place at your company?
3. Has your company conducted an energy audit to identify opportunities to save money by using less energy? If not, why not?
4. List the actions that your organization can take to improve in the following areas:
   a. Creating training programs that identify and implement pollution-prevention opportunities
   b. Switching from paper-based systems to electronic systems
   c. Reducing the number of standalone printers
   d. Adjusting printer settings and processes
   e. Adopting power-management practices for computers
   f. Improving energy efficiency for your data centers
   g. Reducing food and beverage waste
   h. Reducing unnecessary packaging
   i. Improving your transportation and fleet efficiency
   j. Creating green teams at your organization
5. Has your company explored the use of DfE and LCAs to reduce the use of toxic chemicals and identify new business and market opportunities?
6. What green-building practices do you have in place for your organization? Would LEED certification help your organization accomplish its environmental and financial goals??
7. Does your company participate in any carbon-offset programs? If not, you may want to do a financial analysis to see if this is a good option for your business.

Chapter 5 Endnotes

1. Edward O. Wilson, *Half-Earth: Our Planet's Fight for Life* (New York: Liveright, 2017), 57–58.

2. Jennifer Bennett, The Ocean Portal Team, and NOAA, "Ocean Acidification." Ocean Portal | Smithsonian. May 14, 2018. Accessed June 12, 2018. https://ocean.si.edu/ocean-life/invertebrates/ocean-acidification.

3. Personal experience from managing training programs, including Waste$mart.

4. Department of Energy, "About the Commercial Buildings Integration Program." Accessed June 12, 2018. https://www.energy.gov/eere/buildings/about-commercial-buildings-integration-program.

5. Ian M. Shapiro, *Energy Audits and Improvements for Commercial Buildings* (Hoboken: Wiley, 2016), 6.

6. World Wildlife Fund, "Use paper more efficiently." Accessed June 12, 2018. http://wwf.panda.org/get_involved/live_green/fsc/save_paper/office_paper/use_paper_more_efficiently/.

7. Daniel C. Esty and P. J. Simmons, *The Green to Gold Business Playbook: How to Implement Sustainability Practices for Bottom-Line Results in Every Business Function* (Hoboken: John Wiley & Sons, 2011), 130.

8. Energy Star, "Put Your Computers to Sleep." Central Air Conditioners and Air Source Heat Pumps. Accessed June 12, 2018. https://www.energystar.gov/products/low_carbon_it_campaign/put_your_computers_sleep.

9. Steve Ryan, "Computer Power Management." College Planning & Management. October 1, 2014. Accessed June 12, 2018. https://webcpm.com/Articles/2014/10/01/Computer-Power-Management.aspx.

10. Ibid.

11. Note 8, supra.

12. Ibid.

13. Ibid.

14. Walmart, "2016 Global Responsibility Report," 77. Accessed June 26, 2018. https://corporate.walmart.com/2016grr.

15. Ibid.

16. Ibid.

17. Genentech, "Green Genes: Breakthrough Science. One Moment, One Day, One Person at a Time." Accessed June 12, 2018. https://www.gene.com/good/sustainability/green-genes.

18. Automobili Lamborghini, "Lamborghini Automobili Spa." Accessed June 5, 2017. https://www.lamborghini.com/en-en/company.
19. Hewlett Packard, "Environment." Accessed June 5, 2015. http://www8.hp.com/us/en/hp-information/environment/footprint.html.
20. Ibid.
21. Ibid.
22. U.S. Green Building Council, "The Business Case for Green Building." February 10, 2015. Accessed June 12, 2018. https://www.usgbc.org/articles/business-case-green-building.
23. Ibid.
24. Ibid.
25. Ibid.
26. Ibid.
27. Ibid.
28. Ibid.
29. Adobe, "Corporate Responsibility." Adobe Captivate—Welcome to the World of Smart ELearning Authoring. Accessed January 8, 2018. https://www.adobe.com/corporate-responsibility/sustainability/green-building.html.
30. Ibid.
31. Note 22, supra.
32. Dow, Swiss Re, Shell, Unilever, and The Nature Conservancy, "The Case for Green Infrastructure: Joint-Industry White Paper." June 2013. https://www.nature.org/about-us/the-case-for-green-infrastructure.pdf, 4.
33. Thompson Reuters, "Carbon Market Monitor: Review of 2015 and Outlook for 2016–2018." January 11, 2016, 3. http://climateobserver.org/wp-content/uploads/2016/01/Carbon-Market-Review-2016.pdf.
34. Ibid.
35. Nazila Babakhani, Brent W. Ritchie, and Sara Dolnicar, "Improving Carbon Offsetting Appeals in Online Airplane Ticket Purchasing: Testing New Messages, and Using New Test Methods." Journal of Sustainable Tourism 25, no. 7 (2016): 955-69. doi:10.1080/09669582.2016.1257013.
36. Kelley Hamrick and Melissa Gallant, *Unlocking Potential: State of the Voluntary Carbon Markets 2017* (Washington, DC: Forest Trends' Ecosystem Marketplace, 2016), 3.
37. Ibid.

38. Stanford University, "Allowing polluters to offset carbon emissions by paying forest owners effectively reduces greenhouse gases, Stanford study finds | Stanford News." August 14, 2017. Accessed June 13, 2018. https://news.stanford.edu/2017/08/14/carbon-offsets-wide-ranging-environmental-benefits/.

39. Ibid.

40. Ibid.

CHAPTER 6

Overharvesting: Profitable-Conservation Strategies

"The good man is the friend of all living things."
—Mahatma Gandhi

Overharvesting

We've made it to our final letter of the HIPPO biodiversity-threat acronym (habitat destruction, invasive species, pollution, human overpopulation, and overharvesting). So far, we've covered the biodiversity threats of habitat destruction, invasive species, and pollution. As you can see, the letter "O" in HIPPO stands for "overharvesting." You'll notice that we skipped the second "P" (human overpopulation) since that's a topic most corporations will understandably avoid like the plague.

"Overharvesting" is a broad term that refers to the harvesting of a renewable resource at a rate that is unsustainable. The term can apply to plants, fish stocks, forests, grazing pastures, and game animals. The motivation behind hunting, fishing, and plant collection may be for food, economic reasons, cultural reasons, or sport. Regardless of the reason, overharvesting implies that changes need to be made to current harvesting practices or else animal and plant populations may not recover. The result can be species extinction at the population or species level, and major ecosystem disturbances due to imbalances in predator–prey relationships.

Unfortunately, we've seen many examples of overharvesting over the years—everything from passenger pigeons, tigers, rhinos, and certain species of fish. Let's look at passenger pigeons as an example.

When famous naturalist and artist John James Audubon was on a trip to St. Louis, Missouri, he noticed a sky that was darkened by a large flock of passenger pigeons flying overhead. He described the flock as having no beginning and no end, and the flock continued as a steady stream for three days. Audubon noted that the droppings resembled snowflakes, but I'm guessing that nobody ran outside to catch them on their tongue. As the story goes, Audubon started to count the number of pigeons that he could see in the sky, but he soon gave up. There were too many to count. Today, it's quite easy to count how many passenger pigeons are in the sky: zero. They are extinct.

In the late 1700s and early 1800s, passenger pigeons were one of the most abundant bird species in the world, with an estimated population of three to five billion birds.[1] That's twice the number of people on Earth at the time.[2] In only 100 years, passenger pigeons were wiped out of existence, primarily through hunting.

The last verified record of a wild passenger pigeon was in March 1900, when a boy in Pike County, Ohio, shot the bird because it was eating corn at his farm.[3] That left just a few remaining passenger pigeons in a single captive flock at the Cincinnati Zoo. Breeding attempts failed, and the flock dwindled until there was only one left: Martha. A US$ 1,000 reward was offered to anyone who could find a mate for Martha, but none was found. On September 1, 1914, Martha—the last known passenger pigeon—died at the Cincinnati Zoo at the age of 29.[4] Martha's body is periodically on display at the Smithsonian Institution in Washington, DC, and a memorial statue of Martha can be found at the Cincinnati Zoo aviary.

Even if you consider pigeons to be flying rats, the story of the passenger pigeon's demise still represents a failure of epic proportions when it comes to fulfilling our responsibility to be good stewards of the environment.

In the 1800s, the idea that a species could be hunted to extinction was a foreign concept to most people. Now that we're in the 2000s, I would like to be able to say that we've learned our lesson; unfortunately, we're not quite there yet. Overharvesting is alive and well. For example, unsustainable fishing practices, such as bottom trawling and blast fishing, are still practiced today, and we've seen significant declines in several commercial fish populations, such as Atlantic halibut, to the point where their survival is threatened.

Tigers and rhinos have been overhunted, primarily for traditional medicines derived from various parts of these magnificent animals. While it's illegal to hunt and kill tigers and rhinos, the economic incentive from Asian medicinal markets is so great that the hunting of these endangered animals continues. In Vietnam, a rhino horn can be worth up to US$ 100,000 per kilogram. Since a typical rhino horn weighs anywhere from 1 to 3 kilograms, depending on the species, one horn can be worth over US$ 300,000.[5] Rhino horns are also sought after in Yemen where the horn is used for the handles of curved daggers called "jambiya," which are presented to Yemeni boys at the age of 12 as a symbol of manhood and status.

Thankfully, we may be rounding the corner for some charismatic animal species, such as the tiger. For the first time in more than a century, the world population of tigers is on the rise. The number of tigers has increased from 3,200 to 3,890 from 2010 to 2016.[6] However, there's still much work to be done to keep this trend heading in the right direction.

Let's not forget about plants. Roughly 75% of the top 150 prescription drugs in the United States are based on natural sources, and over 25% of prescribed medicines in developed countries are derived from wild plants.[7] We've also seen a multibillion-dollar boom in the herbal market, fueled largely by a desire to find "natural approaches" to medicine. In addition, up to 80% of people in developing countries are totally dependent on herbal drugs for their primary healthcare.[8] When you add all of this up, it's no surprise that medicinal plants are facing significant overharvesting pressures. Roughly 15,000 species of the 50,000 to 80,000 flowering plant species used for medicinal purposes worldwide are threatened with extinction from overharvesting and habitat destruction.[9]

Profitable-Conservation Strategies for Overharvesting

Corporations have an important role to play in preventing the overharvesting of plants and animals. This applies to all companies—not just the ones in the fishery, pharmaceutical, and herbal-medicine industries that directly source plants and animals. The best way that most companies large and small can help prevent overharvesting is to "green" their supply chain. Greening the supply chain is also an effective strategy for combating other biodiversity threats, such as habitat destruction and pollution.

Let's start with a few definitions to make sure we're on the same page.

"Supply-chain management" refers to the activities that enable the right product to get to the right consumer, in the right quantity, at the right time. This includes the steps that occur from raw-materials extraction to consumer purchase, such as planning, forecasting, purchasing, product assembly, transportation, storage, distribution, sales, customer service, and product returns. The goal of supply-chain management is to deliver products better, faster, and cheaper.

"Greening the supply chain" adds an environmental lens to traditional supply-chain management practices. This may include a variety of environment-focused actions that guide a company's interactions with its various suppliers, including:

- Setting environmental standards that all suppliers must meet
- Creating performance goals, metrics, and supplier scorecards that are used to monitor and evaluate supplier performance over time
- Establishing a supplier-audit program to verify that suppliers have successfully implemented processes that are effective in reducing environmental impacts
- Improving business processes to reduce environmental impacts
- Identifying alternative materials that have a smaller environmental footprint
- Partnering with government agencies, industry groups, and nongovernment organizations (NGOs) to look for new ways to improve environmental performance

In this section, we'll focus our attention on two of these strategies: supplier scorecards and supplier audits.

Greening the Supply Chain Strategy #1: Supplier Scorecards

Supplier scorecards can be an effective way to integrate environmental concerns in purchasing decisions, if they're done right. A "supplier scorecard" includes the processes and tools that are used to collect data to measure, rate, or rank suppliers. The end product is typically a report or table that summarizes supplier performance across various categories of interest. The categories may be weighted differently and added up to generate an overall weighted score, which includes factors like cost, quality, and a variety of sustainability and environmental-impact measures.

Some companies use the same scorecard for all suppliers and all products; other companies create category-specific scorecards, which contain questions that are only used for a certain product category, such as electronics, apparel, and paper products. A one-size-fits-all scorecard typically contains generic environmental measures, such as energy use, water-use efficiency, greenhouse-gas emissions, and the amount of solid and hazardous waste that is generated and disposed. A category-specific scorecard will include questions that address specific environmental impacts associated with that product category. For example, an environmental scorecard for food or personal-care products may include a measure like the percentage of responsibility-sourced palm oil. Companies that adopt a category approach may end up with 100 or more category-specific scorecards.

No standard supplier scorecard or measurement approach is used across industries. However, companies may join organizations, such as The Sustainability Consortium, which share best practices and help drive consistency across product categories. At a high level, here are some best practices for designing and implementing a well-designed scorecard program from an environmental perspective:

- **Management support.** To have environmental considerations taken seriously in purchasing decisions, your first task is to get management support. This includes the chief executive officer and the rest of the C-Suite as well as key managers in purchasing, product design, and supply-chain management. To do this, you'll need to put together a persuasive business case that shows how the inclusion of environmental considerations in purchasing decisions will add value to the business.
- **Integration of environment and business.** The environmental portion of a supplier scorecard shouldn't be managed as a separate effort that is tucked away in your company's sustainability office. The environmental portion of a supplier-scorecard program should be considered part of the existing business process, not a separate check-the-box process that people feel obligated to do to keep the sustainability team happy. You'll want to have an environmental manager join business-planning sessions and supplier reviews as one of the voices at the table. This person should be able to effectively communicate the value proposition of how environmental measures and targets add value to the company and how the collected data will be used to help the company meet those targets.

- **Incentives for buyers.** Your organization should create financial rewards and provide recognition for buyers who excel in meeting environmental targets. This can be done in several ways. You can include specific environmental targets as part of a division or a business unit's overall performance objectives. Another option is to provide individual rewards and recognition, such as financial bonuses, gift cards, or certificates, which are handed out by senior leaders at department or all-hands meetings. Finally, you can display each person's environmental performance on an intranet site or on a bulletin board or whiteboard in your department. This creates some healthy competition to earn the top spot and provides an incentive for those at the bottom of the list to improve their performance.
- **Incentives for suppliers.** Ditto for suppliers. You can create financial incentives that motivate suppliers to meet or exceed environmental targets. For starters, you'll want to ensure that scorecards are getting sufficient visibility. To help with this issue of visibility, you can require senior managers at each supplier to review and acknowledge receipt of the scorecard. You can also let suppliers know how they rank against other suppliers and provide rewards and recognition for top suppliers. For low-performing suppliers, you can set up meetings to discuss their results and offer suggestions on how they can improve their performance moving forward.
- **Tools and training.** If you decide to roll out a supplier-sustainability scorecard, then you'll want to ensure that all impacted teammates receive the appropriate level of training, tools, and support to enable them to hit the ground running. The training sessions should reinforce the value proposition of including environmental concerns in purchasing decisions and give you an opportunity to tell your teammates about the rewards and recognition program in place.

■ Greening the Supply Chain Strategy #2: Supplier Audits

When it comes to working with suppliers, many corporations adopt a policy of "trust but verify." When a supplier reports that it's delivering sustainably sourced wood and other materials, is following all applicable regulations, and is meeting the terms of your supplier code of conduct, that's all great news;

however, you'll want to gather more data to confirm that this is truly the case. After all, a company's supply chain often represents one of the greatest areas of legal exposure for a corporation. To do this, a corporation will set up a supplier-audit program.

The scope of a supplier audit includes more than just environmental issues. It will also encompass topics like worker safety, fraud, bribes, child labor, and conflicts of interest; however, we'll only discuss environmental issues in this section. Let's look at the steps of a basic process.

◆ Step #1: Create a supply-chain map.

In this step, you'll identify your suppliers as well as your suppliers' suppliers. This will help you identify areas where you should focus your attention.

◆ Step #2: Identify high-risk suppliers.

You probably won't want to audit every supplier; instead, you'll want to focus on suppliers that are considered a high risk based on their potential to jeopardize your product quality, reputation, continuity of supply, or operating costs. You may want to categorize your suppliers as high, medium, and low risk based on these factors as well as their relative size and historical performance.

◆ Step #3: Determine the audit scope and approach for each supplier.

You may want to create different audit methodologies for low-, medium-, and high-risk suppliers. More intensive audit processes, including on-site visits, should be reserved for high-risk suppliers.

◆ Step #4: Conduct research on a supplier's environmental performance.

This can be done through a search of publicly available sources as well as reports and data that you receive directly from your suppliers. You may need to create some questions to collect specific information that's not typically covered in supplier reports or publicly available sources.

◆ Step #5: Conduct on-site audits for key suppliers.

These on-site audits should include periodic, unannounced visits. You may need to specify your desire for periodic, unannounced visits in your supplier code of conduct to avoid pushback when you show up unexpectedly at their door.

◆ Step #6: Collaborate to improve process efficiency and product sustainability.

This last step is often missing from the supplier-audit process. Rather than treat the audit solely as a risk-exposure exercise, use the audit as an opportunity to make process and product improvements that have the potential to save money while reducing environmental impacts. For example, you can work together to look for ways to improve transportation efficiency, reduce the amount of packaging waste, and share best practices that you've gathered from other suppliers or companies.

In recent years, supplier audits have been the subject of some criticism. There's a perception that audits aren't effective in detecting, reporting, or correcting environmental issues in the supply chain. There's also a concern that supplier deception is rampant but hard to detect. Based on some of the audits I've conducted over the years, I must agree that suppliers tend to provide information and data that paint a rosy picture of their performance and are reluctant to share information and data that will expose weaknesses.

The best way to address these valid concerns is to conduct unannounced site visits for high-risk suppliers. Of course, these may not always be practical or feasible, depending on the nature of operations and the terms of the supplier agreement in place. During your visit, it's helpful to start with a thorough walk-through of the site. As part of the site walk-through, you'll want to randomly interview people along the way, asking a few questions that can uncover potential issues for that area of the business. The key is to ask questions from the perspective of curiosity and interest from a business partner rather than in an accusatory or threatening manner from a suspicious customer. If you set the tone up front that you're looking for ways to reduce risks, improve process efficiency, and reduce the environmental impacts of the products you purchase from a life-cycle perspective, then you're more likely to have suppliers that partner with you to identify and improve weaknesses rather than suppliers that are deceptive and defensive.

Let's look at Walmart as an example since they've done an excellent job in pulling together each of these best practices in their supplier-scorecard program for the company's 100,000+ suppliers.

For its scorecard design, Walmart initially started with a one-size-fits-all approach that included 15 basic questions for all suppliers. Walmart has since switched to a category approach, choosing from more than 100 category-specific questions that are tied to specific products. These questions were pulled together with some help from assessment criteria developed by The Sustainability Consortium, of which Walmart is a member.

Supplier responses are scored on a scale of 1 to 100, and suppliers are then ranked within a product category. Walmart shares this category ranking with each supplier, so they know where they stand, but suppliers aren't given the names of the suppliers that scored above or below them. To its credit, Walmart also provides each supplier with suggested areas for improvement that will help them improve process efficiency, deliver more sustainable products, and improve their category ranking.

Regarding incentives and rewards, Walmart includes sustainability goals as part of each buyer's performance objectives. Performance is reviewed annually, and Walmart issues a Sustainable Buyer of the Year award for each business unit, which includes a financial reward. Incentives are also in place for high- and low-performing suppliers. High performers receive recognition and perks like special placement on e-commerce sites. Low performers are invited to a Walmart "family meeting" to discuss their performance and opportunities for improvement. To ensure that buyers and suppliers have the training and tools they need to succeed, Walmart provides sustainability-program training as well as Buyer Tool Kits that include reference guides and other job-specific guidance.

As for auditing, Walmart sets up-front expectations with suppliers that the company will monitor supply-chain conditions through audits and investigations. Walmart assigns each facility to one of three risk categories based on World Bank data for the facility's location. Each category has the following audit requirements:

- **Category 1: Lower Risk.** Facilities in these countries are not required to complete an audit on a regular schedule; instead, Walmart will select a sample of facilities to audit each year.
- **Category 2: Medium Risk.** These facilities are required to complete an audit and follow-up audits as specified by the supplier's chosen third-party audit program.

- **Category 3: Higher Risk.** These facilities have the same requirements as Category 2 countries, and new facilities must submit a prequalification audit.

Walmart then reviews third-party audit reports that are submitted by suppliers and assigns a rating to each facility. The most common facility ratings include the following:

- **Green.** High level of compliance with Walmart's Standards for Suppliers
- **Yellow.** General compliance with the Standards for Suppliers
- **Orange.** More serious violations of the Standards for Suppliers, but Walmart will continue to allow sourcing while the violations are remediated. Three consecutive orange ratings may change the rating to red.
- **Red.** Violations of a nature that may make it appropriate to temporarily or permanently terminate a facility's ability to supply products for Walmart.

Walmart assessors also review report findings to look for higher-risk issues that may change a facility's color rating from orange to red. These cases may be escalated for possible investigation or supplier engagement.

In addition to monitoring facility audit findings, Walmart will investigate a facility if it learns of allegations that a supplier violated Walmart's Standards for Suppliers. These allegations are investigated regardless of the facility risk category. Allegations may surface from audit-program findings, the Walmart Ethics hotline and inbox, anonymous tips, internal business partners, as well as NGO and media reports. If the findings prove to be true, then Walmart will either proceed with a corrective action plan or termination of the supplier contract.

Profitability of Greening the Supply Chain as a Conservation Strategy

Greening the supply chain is definitely a profitable-conservation strategy—just ask Dell Computer. Dell holds supplier-innovation summits to generate new ideas for improvements across all areas of the supply chain. For example, one supplier-innovation summit generated the idea that it can remove toxic paints from some of its computers and replace it with a much safer film covering.

Another Dell supplier came up with the idea to mix in straw grass with wood-based pulp for some of Dell's corrugate boxes. Straw grass is a more quickly renewable resource compared to trees. In addition, straw grass is burned as a farming waste product in parts of China. Rather than burn the straw grass, it could be utilized in the corrugate boxes. Because of this suggestion, Dell now uses a mix of 30% straw grass pulp in some of its boxes.[10] Dell's innovation program has reduced supply-chain costs by roughly US$ 100 million annually for the past two years.[11] In addition, Dell is on track to reach about 90% of its 2020 sustainability goals.[12]

Dell is not alone. In 2013, Walmart announced that it saved US$ 150 million from supply-chain sustainability efforts in that year alone.[13] General Motors established a reusable-container program with its suppliers and was able to reduce disposal costs by US$ 12 million while reducing environmental impacts.[14] Texas Instruments saves about US$ 8 million per year through supply-chain management practices, such as reducing source materials and reducing and reusing packaging.[15]

As you can see from the examples above, greening your supply chain can add real value to your business by cutting costs, driving innovation for new products and processes, improving customer and consumer perception of your company, and helping you meet or exceed environmental regulations and performance targets.

Preventing Overharvesting through Technology

Greening the supply chain isn't the only strategy that corporations pursue when it comes to preventing overharvesting. Some companies are leveraging their technology to help prevent hunting of endangered wildlife.

For example, Cisco Systems has partnered with Dimension Data on a Connected Conservation initiative to track rhino poachers at a game reserve in South Africa. Cisco and Dimension Data are using seismic sensors, drone cameras, thermal imaging, biometric scanning, and networking technology to track the movements of all humans who enter the reserve grounds. Park rangers use these new tools in combination with traditional sniffer dogs and trained soldiers on the ground to catch and deter poachers while minimizing disturbances to the endangered rhinos. The results have been impressive so far. The Connected Conservation initiative has been successful in reducing rhino poaching at the South African reserve by 96%.[16]

In the future, this approach may be leveraged to protect other endangered species throughout the world. The main obstacle that prevents the spread of this technological approach is the US$ 1.5 million-per-year cost of the system.[17] More and more companies are leveraging their products and technologies to develop solutions that directly help in the fight against overharvesting.

Chapter 6 Action Steps

1. Describe how your company contributes to the problems of overharvesting.
2. What steps does your company take to minimize the threat of overharvesting?
3. Do you use a supplier scorecard to guide your purchasing decisions and are environmental impacts included as part of that scorecard? If not, why not?
4. Do you have a supplier-auditing program in place to help ensure that your suppliers are meeting their environmental commitments? If not, why not?
5. What positive incentives or rewards can you put in place to encourage your suppliers to partner with you to develop and implement innovations that save money while reducing environmental impacts?
6. Does your company have technology that can be leveraged to support efforts to prevent overharvesting?

Chapter 6 Endnotes

1. Smithsonian Institution, "The Passenger Pigeon." Accessed June 13, 2018. https://www.si.edu/spotlight/passenger-pigeon.
2. Our World in Data, "World Population Growth." Accessed June 13, 2018. https://ourworldindata.org/world-population-growth.
3. The Pike County News Watchman, "From Billions to Buttons: The Demise of the Passenger Pigeon." May 2, 2014. Accessed June 13, 2018. https://www.newswatchman.com/blogs/rural_rendezvous/article_bee70f2a-5d85-5210-b53f-8e06c6aeee87.html.

4. Note 1, supra.

5. Gwynn Guilford, "Why Does a Rhino Horn Cost $300,000? Because Vietnam Thinks It Cures Cancer and Hangovers." The Atlantic. May 15, 2013. Accessed June 13, 2018. https://www.theatlantic.com/business/archive/2013/05/why-does-a-rhino-horn-cost-300-000-because-vietnam-thinks-it-cures-cancer-and-hangovers/275881/.

6. World Wildlife Fund, "For the first time in 100 years, tiger numbers are growing." April 10, 2016. Accessed June 13, 2018. https://www.worldwildlife.org/stories/for-the-first-time-in-100-years-tiger-numbers-are-growing.

7. Shi-Lin Chen, Hua Yu, Hong-Mei Luo, Qiong Wu, Chun-Fang Li, and André Steinmetz, "Conservation and Sustainable Use of Medicinal Plants: Problems, Progress, and Prospects." Chinese Medicine 11, no. 1 (2016). doi:10.1186/s13020-016-0108-7.

8. Ibid.

9. Ibid.

10. GreenSCM, "Green Supply Chain News: Dell Turn to Innovation to Meet Sustainability Goals." "Green Supply Chain News: Nike Promises Revolution in Its Approach to Manufacturing." October 4, 2016. Accessed June 13, 2018. http://thegreensupplychain.com/news/16-10-04-1.php?cid=11349.

11. Ibid.

12. Ibid.

13. Garrett McCullum, "Greening the supply chain to up profits, cut costs and get ahead." VentureBeat. April 11, 2018. Accessed June 13, 2018. https://venturebeat.com/2012/12/19/greening-the-supply-chain/.

14. Mark Millar, *Global Supply Chain Ecosystems: Strategies for Competitive Advantage in a Complex, Connected World* (London: Kogan Page, 2015), 53.

15. Daniel C. Esty and P. J. Simmons, *The Green to Gold Business Playbook: How to Implement Sustainability Practices for Bottom-Line Results in Every Business Function* (Hoboken: John Wiley & Sons, 2011), 55.

16. Blogs@Cisco—Cisco Blogs, "Expanding Connected Conservation in 2018." May 8, 2018. Accessed June 13, 2018. https://blogs.cisco.com/news/expanding-connected-conservation-in-2018.

17. CNN, "Can 'connected' conservation save the rhino?" August 25, 2016. Accessed June 13, 2018. https://www.cnn.com/2016/08/25/africa/rhino-data-conservation-mpa/index.html.

CHAPTER 7

Sustainability Reporting: The Biodiversity Section

"Torture numbers, and they'll confess to anything."
—Greg Easterbrook, in *The New Republic*

Sustainability Reporting

Believe it or not, sustainability reporting played a significant role in my motivation to write this book. Why, you ask? Well, as a certified sustainability-reporting geek, I like to flip through the biodiversity sections of corporate social responsibility initiatives, sustainability reports, and biodiversity-related pages on company websites to see what companies are up to. Do I know how to party, or what?

When I read these sources, I'm often dismayed by the weakness of the write-ups when it comes to addressing biodiversity and wildlife conservation. In many reports, there's no mention of biodiversity or wildlife conservation at all; in others, I'll find one or two vague sentences about striving to minimize impacts to biodiversity. It's hard to find solid write-ups that communicate an understanding of how the company impacts biodiversity and wildlife, why it's important for the business to consider these things, and what steps the company is taking to address the different threats. In this chapter, I hope to provide some guidance on how companies can bridge this gap.

Let's start with a primer on sustainability reporting. A "sustainability report" is a document that provides an overview of a company's economic, environmental, and social impacts that are caused by its everyday activities. There are three major sustainability reporting standards: the Sustainability Accounting Standards Board (SASB), the Integrated Reporting Framework of the International Integrated Reporting Council (IIRC), and the Global Reporting Initiative (GRI). Each standard takes a slightly different approach to the sustainability reporting, so let's look at each one in more detail.

The Sustainability Accounting Standards Board

Founded in 2011, the SASB is a nonprofit organization based out of San Francisco, California. The organization seeks to develop and maintain sustainability-accounting standards that help public corporations disclose useful information to investors in U.S. Securities and Exchange Commission (SEC) filings. The SASB strives to serve as an independent, standards-setting organization that "envisions a world where a shared understanding of corporate sustainability performance allows companies and investors to make informed decisions that drive value and improve sustainability outcomes."[1]

The SASB's approach is to work with the current system of financial regulation in the United States by integrating its sustainability standards into Form 10-K, which all public companies must file with the SEC. To do this, the SASB created 79 industry-specific sustainability standards that focus on the factors that are likely to have material impacts for each industry.

The SASB has also created a Materiality Map™ (https://materiality.sasb.org) that shows, at a glance, which sustainability issues are considered material for each industry. For example, "biodiversity impacts" are listed as one of the issues mapped to each industry. Other environmental impacts listed in the Materiality Map include greenhouse-gas emissions, air quality, energy management, fuel management, water and wastewater management, and waste and hazardous materials management.

Here is a summary of the biodiversity-reporting standards and information that companies in each industry are expected to provide in their reports under the SASB framework.

Warning: The following list of the SASB's standards may make your eyes glaze over, but I included it anyway because it's helpful in understanding why some companies report on biodiversity impacts while others do not.

- The Health Care sector is divided into six industries: Biotechnology, Pharmaceuticals, Medical Equipment and Supplies, Health Care Delivery, Health Care Distribution, and Managed Care. According to the Materiality Map, biodiversity impacts are not likely to be material for any of these industries. This surprised me, as I expected to see the Pharmaceuticals industry listed due its bio-prospecting and purchasing activities that have the potential to significantly impact biodiversity.
- The Financials sector includes seven industries: Commercial Banks, Investment Banking and Brokerage, Asset Management and Custody Activities, Consumer Finance, Mortgage Finance, Security and Commodity Exchanges, and Insurance. None of these industries were listed as having a material impact on biodiversity. However, I wouldn't be shocked if this "no-material-impact" status changes in the future as biodiversity issues become increasingly important from a risk-management perspective.
- The Technology and Communications sector includes six industries: Electronic Manufacturing Services and Original Design Manufacturing, Software and Information Technology Services, Hardware, Semiconductors, Telecommunications, and Internet Media and Services. Once again, the SASB's Materiality Map indicates that biodiversity impacts will not likely be material for any of these industries.
- The Non-Renewable Resources sector includes the following industries and associated standards:
  - **Oil and Gas—Exploration and Production.** Biodiversity issues are considered a "likely material issue" for companies in this industry. The biodiversity-related accounting metrics and reporting information that companies in this industry should provide in their sustainability reports include the following:
    - Description of environmental-management policies and practices for active sites
    - Number and aggregate volume of hydrocarbon spills, volume in Arctic, volume near shorelines with Environmental Sensitivity Index rankings 8 to 10, and volume recovered

  - Proved and probable reserves in or near sites with protected conservation status or an endangered-species habitat.
- **Oil and Gas—Midstream.** Biodiversity issues are considered a likely material issue. Here are the associated SASB accounting metrics and reporting information for biodiversity impacts:
  - Description of environmental-management policies and practices for active operations
  - Percentage of land owned, leased, and / or operated within areas of protected conservation status or an endangered-species habitat
  - Terrestrial acreage disturbed, percentage of impacted area restored
  - Number and aggregate volume of hydrocarbon spills, volume in Arctic, volume in Unusually Sensitive Areas, and volume recovered
- **Oil and Gas—Refining and Marketing.** Biodiversity issues are not a likely material issue.
- **Oil and Gas—Services.** Biodiversity issues are not a likely material issue.
- **Coal Operations.** Biodiversity issues are considered a likely material issue. Companies should provide the following in their sustainability reports:
  - Description of environmental-management policies and practices for active sites
  - Percentage of mine sites where acid rock drainage is: (1) predicted to occur, (2) actively mitigated, and (3) under treatment or remediation
  - Proven and probable reserves in or near sites with protected conservation status or an endangered-species habitat
- **Iron and Steel Producers.** Biodiversity issues are not a likely material issue.
- **Metals and Mining.** Biodiversity issues are considered a likely material issue. Companies should provide the following in their sustainability reports:

    - Description of environmental-management policies and practices for active sites
    - Percentage of mine sites where acid rock drainage is: (1) predicted to occur, (2) actively mitigated, and (3) under treatment or remediation
    - Proven and probable reserves in or near sites with protected conservation status or an endangered-species habitat
  - **Construction Materials.** Biodiversity issues are considered a likely material issue. Companies should provide the following in their sustainability reports:
    - Description of environmental-management policies and practices for active sites
    - Terrestrial acreage disturbed, percentage of impacted area restored
- The Transportation sector includes eight industries: Automobiles, Auto Parts, Car Rentals & Leasing, Airlines, Air Freight & Logistics, Marine Transportation, Rail Transportation, and Road Transportation. Biodiversity issues are not considered a likely material issue for companies in these industries except for the Marine Transportation industry.
  - **Marine Transportation:** Here is the SASB accounting metric that companies should include in sustainability reports: number and aggregate volume of spills and releases to the environment.
- The Services sector includes 10 industries: Education, Professional Services, Hotels & Lodging, Casinos & Gaming, Restaurants, Leisure Facilities, Cruise Lines, Advertising & Marketing, Media Production & Distribution, and Cable & Satellite. According to SASB's Materiality Map, biodiversity impacts are not likely to be material for any of these industries except for the Hotels & Lodging and Cruise Lines industries.
  - **Hotels & Lodging:** Companies in this industry should include the following in their sustainability reports:
    - Number of lodging facilities in or near areas of protected-conservation status or an endangered-species habitat

    - Description of environmental-management policies and practices to preserve ecosystem services

  - **Cruise Lines:** Companies in the Cruise Lines industry should include the following metric in their sustainability reports:
    - Cruise duration in marine-protected areas and areas of protected-conservation status

- The Resource Transformation sector includes five industries: Chemicals, Aerospace and Defense, Electrical and Electronic Equipment, Industrial Machinery and Goods, and Containers and Packaging. Biodiversity issues are not considered a likely material issue for companies in these industries, not even in the Chemicals industry. We'll see if that changes in the years to come as more data are collected.
- The Consumption sector is a large one, with 15 industries: Agricultural Products; Meat, Poultry, and Dairy; Processed Foods; Non-Alcoholic Beverages; Alcoholic Beverages; Tobacco; Household and Personal Products; Food Retailers and Distributors; Drug Retailers and Convenience Stores; Multiline and Specialty Retailers and Distributors; E-Commerce; Apparel Accessories and Footwear; Appliance Manufacturing; Building Products and Furnishings; and Toys and Sporting Goods. Biodiversity issues are considered a likely material issue for companies in two of these industries: Agricultural Products as well as Meat, Poultry, and Dairy.
  - **Agricultural Products**
    - Description of strategies to manage land use and ecological impacts
    - Amount of pesticide consumption by hazard level
    - Amount of fertilizer consumption by nitrogen-based, phosphate-based, and potassium-based fertilizers.
  - **Meat, Poultry and Dairy**
    - Percentage of pasture and grazing land managed to Natural Resources Conservation Service Conservation Plan criteria.
- The Renewable Resources and Alternative Energy sector contains six industries: Biofuels, Solar Energy, Wind Energy, Fuel Cells and Industrial Batteries, Forestry and Logging, and Pulp and Paper

Products. Biodiversity issues are considered a likely material issue for companies for companies in the Solar Energy, Wind Energy, and Forestry and Logging industries. When I first read this list, I jumped up and said, "Why not Pulp and Paper Products?" Then I read that the Pulp and Paper industry standard includes an environmental impact category called "Fiber Sourcing & Recovery," which includes requirements to report on the percentage of wood fiber sourced from third-party-certified forestlands, a breakdown of the percentage for each fiber-sourcing standard, and the amount of recycled and recovered fiber procured. Whew. Now, let's get back to the requirements for the Solar Energy, Wind Energy, and Forestry and Logging industries.

- **Solar Energy**
  - Amount of project development asset write-offs (in U.S. dollars) that resulted from asset impairments associated with community or ecological impacts
  - Description of efforts in solar-energy system project development to address community and ecological impacts
- **Wind Energy**
  - Amount of turbine order backlog (in U.S. dollars) that was subject to cancellation during the fiscal year for reasons related to or associated with community or ecological impacts
  - Description of efforts to address ecological and community impacts of wind-energy production through turbine design
- **Forestry and Logging**
  - Area of forestland certified to a third-party, forest-management standard, percentage certified to each standard
  - Area of forestland with protected conservation status
  - Area of forestland in an endangered-species habitat
  - Discussion of approach to optimizing opportunities from ecosystem services provided by forestlands

- The Infrastructure sector has eight industries: Electric Utilities; Gas Utilities; Water Utilities; Waste Management; Engineering and Construction Services; Home Builders; Real Estate Owners, Developers, and Investment Trusts; and Real Estate Services. Biodiversity issues are considered a likely material issue for companies in the Engineering and Construction Services and Home Builders industries. I was a bit surprised to see that the Electric Utilities industry was omitted from the list given the biodiversity impacts associated with its extensive water use, transmission-line corridors, and siting of new power-plant infrastructure.
    - **Engineering and Construction Services**
        - Number of incidents of noncompliance with environmental permits, standards, and regulations
        - Discussion of processes to assess and manage environmental risks associated with project design, siting, and construction
    - **Home Builders**
        - Number of lots and homes delivered on redevelopment sites
        - Number of lots and homes delivered in regions with High or Extremely High Baseline Water Stress
        - Amount of legal and regulatory fines and settlements associated with environmental regulations
        - Description of process to integrate environmental considerations into site selection, site design, and site development and construction

Hopefully that provides you with a better understanding of the SASB standards for sustainability reporting that are related to biodiversity. Now, we'll look at a second reporting standard that takes a different approach.

The International Integrated Reporting Council

The IIRC is a global, not-for-profit organization based out of London, England. Established in 2010, the IIRC is composed of a global coalition of regulators, investors, companies, standard setters, nongovernmental organizations, and representatives from the accounting profession. The organization's mission is to "establish integrated reporting and thinking within mainstream business practice as the norm in the public and private sectors."[2]

This raises the question, "What the heck is an 'integrated report'?"

An "integrated report" pulls together analyses of financial and nonfinancial performance into one report. In the words of IIRC, "An integrated report is a concise communication about how an organization's strategy, governance, performance and prospects, in the context of its external environment, lead to the creation of value over the short, medium and long term."[3] The IIRC has adopted six Guiding Principles for integrated reports: strategic focus and future orientation, connectivity of information, stakeholder relationships, materiality; conciseness, reliability and completeness, and consistency and comparability.

The IIRC Framework uses the term "capitals" to refer to resources and relationships that are used to create value over time. These capitals may include financial, manufactured, intellectual, human, social and relationship, and natural capital.

The last piece—natural capital—is where biodiversity fits. "Natural capital" refers to "all renewable and nonrenewable environmental resources and processes that provide goods or services that support the past, current or future prosperity of an organization."[4] The scope of natural capital includes air, water, land, minerals, forests, biodiversity, and ecosystem health.

As opposed to SASB, the IIRC Framework is principles-based, and it doesn't prescribe any key performance indicators or measurement methods. It's up to the authors of each integrated report to determine what aspects are material and should therefore be included in the report. The IIRC Framework does include the following eight Content Elements that should be addressed in an integrated report:

1. **Organizational overview and external environment.** What does the organization do, and what are the circumstances under which it operates?
2. **Governance.** How does the organization's governance structure support its ability to create value in the short, medium, and long term?
3. **Business model.** What is the organization's business model?
4. **Risks and opportunities.** What are the specific risks and opportunities that affect the organization's ability to create value over the short, medium, and long term, and how is the organization dealing with them?

5. **Strategy and resource allocation.** Where does the organization want to go, and how does it intend to get there?
6. **Performance.** To what extent has the organization achieved its strategic objectives for the period, and what are its outcomes in terms of effects on the capitals?
7. **Outlook.** What challenges and uncertainties are the organization likely to encounter in pursuing its strategy, and what are the potential implications for its business model and future performance?
8. **Basis of presentation.** How does the organization determine what matters to include in the integrated report, and how are such matters quantified or evaluated?

In other words, there's no specific biodiversity standard in the IIRC Framework. Instead, it's up to each organization to determine if biodiversity is materially impacted by their business and should be addressed in the report. It's also up to the organization to determine the best way to present quantitative and qualitative biodiversity-impact data that are consistent with the IIRC Guiding Principles and Content Elements.

That should give you a good idea of how IIRC and SASB differ. Now we'll add one more reporting standard to the mix.

Global Reporting Initiative

GRI is an independent, international organization that has been around since 1997. Headquartered in Amsterdam, the Netherlands, GRI publishes the most widely used sustainability-reporting standard, used by more than 7,500 organizations. In 2016, GRI released its most recent standards, which encourage companies to report publicly on their impacts to the economy, the environment, and society. GRI's framework is the one with which I'm most familiar as I received certification in GRI's sustainability reporting framework in 2010.

The GRI Standards are divided into four series: Universal Standards (Series 100), Economic topics (Series 200), Environmental topics (Series 300), and Social topics (Series 400). Using the GRI Standards, companies identify topics that are considered material for its business and follow GRI requirements (must do), recommendations (encouraged to do), and guidance (background information and examples) on how to address those impacts. Report quality is guided by six reporting principles: accuracy, balance, clarity, comparability, reliability, and timeliness.

Report content is guided by four key principles:

1. **Stakeholder inclusiveness.** The reporting organization identifies its stakeholders and explains how it has responded to their reasonable expectations and interests.
2. **Sustainability context.** The report presents the reporting organization's performance in the wider context of sustainability.
3. **Materiality.** The report covers topics that reflect the reporting organization's significant economic, environmental, and social impacts or topics that significantly influence stakeholder assessments and decisions.
4. **Completeness.** The report includes coverage of material topics along with a description of where the impacts occur and the organization's involvement with these impacts. The organization should provide enough information to enable stakeholders to assess the reporting organization's performance in the reporting period.

An organization that wants to claim that its report meets the GRI Standards must comply with either the Core requirements or the Comprehensive requirements specified by GRI. The distinction of Core versus Comprehensive is simply an indicator of the degree to which the GRI Standards have been applied to an organization's report. The Comprehensive option has a longer set of general disclosures and topic-specific disclosures that the organization must report.

The GRI's Biodiversity Standard (GRI 304) includes requirements for an organization to provide a disclosure of its management approach as well as several topic-specific disclosures. The management-approach disclosure is a narrative explanation of how an organization manages biodiversity impacts, a description of its associated impacts, and an overview of stakeholders' reasonable expectations and interests. The management approach can also include a description of the organization's biodiversity-management strategy to prevent, manage, and remediate damage to natural habitats that result from its activities.

The topic-specific disclosure of the Biodiversity Standard includes the following four disclosures:

1. **Disclosure 304-1.** Operational sites owned, leased, managed in, or adjacent to protected areas and areas of high biodiversity value outside protected areas. This should include information about sites for

which future operations have been formally announced. Disclosure 304-1 includes the following reporting requirements:

a. For each operational site owned, leased, managed in, or adjacent to protected areas and areas of high biodiversity value outside protected areas, the reporting organization must report the following information:

    - Geographic location;
    - Subsurface and underground land that may be owned, leased, or managed by the organization;
    - Position in relation to the protected area (in the area, adjacent to, or containing portions of the protected area) or the high biodiversity value area outside protected areas;
    - Type of operation (office, manufacturing or production, or extractive);
    - Size of operational site in km^2 (or another unit, if appropriate);
    - Biodiversity value characterized by the attribute of the protected area or area of high biodiversity value outside the protected area (terrestrial, freshwater, or maritime ecosystem);
    - Biodiversity value characterized by listing of protected status, such as International Union for Conservation of Nature (IUCN) Protected Area Management Categories, Ramsar Convention, and national legislation. IUCN is an organization that assesses the conservation status of species and publishes the IUCN Red List of Threatened Species.

2. **Disclosure 304-2.** Significant impacts of activities, products, and services on biodiversity. This disclosure provides background to better understand an organization's strategy to mitigate direct impacts to biodiversity as well as indirect impacts that may occur through activities in the supply chain. This disclosure includes quantitative data that facilitate comparisons of biodiversity impacts over time and across organizations. Here are the reporting requirements for Disclosure 304-2:

a. Nature of significant direct and indirect impacts on biodiversity with reference to one or more of the following concerns:
   - Construction or use of manufacturing plants, mines, and transport infrastructure
   - Pollution (introduction of substances that do not naturally occur in the habitat from point and nonpoint sources)
   - Introduction of invasive species, pests, and pathogens
   - Reduction of species
   - Habitat conversion
   - Changes in ecological processes outside the natural range of variation, such as salinity or changes in groundwater level

b. Significant direct and indirect positive and negative impacts with reference to the following concerns:
   - Species affected
   - Extent of areas impacted
   - Duration of impacts
   - Reversibility or irreversibility of the impacts

3. **Disclosure 304-3.** Habitats protected or restored. With this disclosure, the organization should discuss any prevention and remediation activities that have an impact on biodiversity. This includes areas where remediation has already been completed or areas that are actively protected.

   An organization can include an area where operations are still active if it meets the definition of "area restored" or "area protected." An "area restored" is defined as an "area that was used during or affected by operational activities, and where remediation measures have either restored the environment to its original state, or to a state where it has a healthy and functioning ecosystem."[5] An "area protected" is defined as an "area that is protected from any harm during operational activities, and where the environment remains in its original state with a healthy and functioning ecosystem."[6]

GRI also recommends that the information presented in this disclosure should align with any applicable regulatory or license requirements for the protection or restoration of habitats.

The reporting disclosures for 304-3 include the following information:

- Size and location of all habitat areas protected or restored, and whether the success of the restoration measure was or is approved by independent external professionals
- Whether partnerships exist with third parties to protect or restore habitat areas distinct from where the organization has overseen and implemented restoration or protection measures
- Status of each area based on its condition at the close of the reporting period
- Standards, methodologies, and assumptions used

4. **Disclosure 304-4.** The IUCN Red List species and national conservation list species with habitats in areas affected by operations. This disclosure helps ensure that an organization identifies areas where its activities pose a threat to endangered plant and animal species. IUCN Red List species and national conservation list species should be compared with the species that the organization listed in its planning documentation and monitoring records.

   The required disclosures for 304-4 include the following information:

   a. Total number of IUCN Red List species and national conservation list species with habitats in areas affected by the operations of the organization, by level of extinction risk:
      - Critically endangered
      - Endangered
      - Vulnerable
      - Near threatened
      - Least concern

Your Sustainability Report's Biodiversity Impact Section Revisited

This section was no doubt a painfully dry read, but I hope this overview of the three different sustainability reporting frameworks has given you a better idea of what stakeholders expect to see in your biodiversity-impact section.

Better yet, I hope the first part of this book has given you a solid understanding of the impact that your organization has on biodiversity and the different steps that you can take to address those impacts. Remember the HIPPO acronym for the biggest threats to biodiversity: habitat destruction, invasive species, pollution, human overpopulation, and overharvesting. That should provide you with a lot more to say than a broad "we consider impacts to biodiversity and wildlife as part of our planning process" type of statement that doesn't provide your stakeholders with much useful information.

Chapter 7 Action Steps

1. What approach or standard does your company follow for reporting sustainability information and data?
2. Does your organization's sustainability report include a section on biodiversity impacts and mitigation strategies? If so, what aspects of HIPPO are included and excluded from the write-up?
3. Based on what you've learned in this book about biodiversity conservation and the HIPPO biodiversity threats and mitigations, what details could you add to your existing sustainability report's biodiversity section to make it more complete? Pass that feedback along to your sustainability report-writing team!

Chapter 7 Endnotes

1. Sustainability Accounting Standards Board, "Mission." Accessed June 14, 2018. https://www.sasb.org/sasb/vision-mission/.
2. Integrated Reporting, "The IIRC." Accessed June 14, 2018. http://integratedreporting.org/the-iirc-2/.
3. International Integrated Reporting Council (2013). The International <IR> Framework: Integrated Reporting, 7. http://integratedreporting.org/wp-content/uploads/2015/03/13-12-08-THE-INTERNATIONAL-IR-FRAMEWORK-2-1.pdf.
4. Ibid., 12.
5. GRI, "GRI Standards Glossary 2016," 2016, 3. https://www.globalreporting.org/standards/media/1035/gri-standards-glossary-2016.pdf.
6. Ibid.

PART 3

Case Studies

Now that we have a solid foundation in the profitable-conservation strategies that businesses can implement that are good for wildlife, biodiversity, and the bottom line, let's look at some additional real-world examples. In the chapters that follow, we'll look at four case studies that showcase companies from different industries and countries to see what they're doing to protect biodiversity and wildlife. For each case study, I've organized the various conservation activities according to four of the five major threats to biodiversity: habitat destruction, invasive species, pollution, and overharvesting.

Whenever possible, I've included quantitative return on investment (ROI) data to give you an idea of what strategies proved to be profitable for these companies. Even though ROI data are often not provided, the mere fact that a company pursues a certain strategy implies that the actions are thought to add value to the organization.

Each case study focuses on the positive steps that these companies are taking in the areas of biodiversity and wildlife conservation. My goal isn't to bash these companies by highlighting what they aren't doing or what they've done wrong over the years. Instead, I'll focus on their positive actions and strategies in the hope that it will generate some ideas that you can use in your organization.

These four companies aren't necessarily the best in their industry at implementing wildlife- and biodiversity-conservation strategies. However, together, they provide us with real-world examples that cover most of the strategies found in this book.

If you would like to read additional profitable-conservation case studies and best practices that include companies from other industries and countries, please visit my website at www.profitableconservation.com.

CHAPTER 8

Profitable-Conservation Case Study: Natura (Brazil)

"We want to create products that combine high technology, the sustainable use of biodiversity and disruptive concepts."
—Natura 2016 Annual Report

Company Overview

For our first profitable-conservation case study, we'll look at a company that operates in one of the biodiversity hotspots of the world. The Amazon. Natura & Co., which is headquartered in São Paulo, Brazil, is in the cosmetics, fragrance, and personal hygiene industry. Natura also happens to be viewed as a global leader in corporate sustainability.

Natura's roughly 900 products are sold under the Natura brand in Brazil, Argentina, Chile, Colombia, France, Mexico, Peru, and the United States. Natura recently expanded its international presence by acquiring the Australian brand Aesop in 2016, and U.K.-based brand The Body Shop in 2017. With the addition of Aesop and The Body Shop, Natura now has over 18,000 employees located in 69 countries.[1]

Natura, Aesop, and The Body Shop have been taking sustainability seriously for many years. Each company has implemented policies to use sustainably sourced ingredients, promote fair trade with suppliers, and prohibit animal testing. Prior to joining Natura, The Body Shop had set a lofty goal to be "the world's most ethical and truly sustainable global business."[2] This fits well with

Natura's 2050 Sustainability Vision to have an overall positive impact from economic, social, environmental, and cultural perspectives on the communities that surround its operations. When it comes to sustainability, these companies are in the big leagues. I was interested to see what Natura is up to when it comes to profitable-conservation strategies for biodiversity and wildlife conservation.

For its sustainability reporting, Natura has adopted both the International Integrated Reporting Council (IIRC) and Global Reporting Initiative (GRI) reporting frameworks. Natura produces one integrated report using IIRC guidelines and includes all the required components of the GRI framework in its integrated report. Natura has been using the GRI framework since 2000, making it the first company in Latin America to do so.

Now that we have that introduction out of the way, let's see what Natura is doing to address four big threats to biodiversity and wildlife: habitat destruction; invasive species; pollution, climate change, and ocean acidification; and overharvesting.

Habitat Destruction

Natura's primary approach to combat habitat destruction is to minimize impacts by greening its supply chain, implementing policies and procedures that promote sustainable operations, and conserving and restoring forests through its carbon-offset program. The company's reports and website don't mention anything about strategies such as installing green roofs, creating wildlife corridors, or purchasing biodiversity offsets. In this section, we'll focus on the steps that Natura is taking to protect biodiversity and wildlife through its supply chain, policies and procedures, and carbon-offset program.

Greening the Supply Chain

Natura is committed to using Brazil's rich biodiversity as the raw materials for its many products, but only if it is harvested in a sustainable way. The company works directly with more than 30 local communities in the Amazon region to help them gather raw materials in a way that keeps the forest healthy and intact, while generating income for 2,119 families in the region. Through this approach, Natura has been able to conserve nearly 635,000 acres of standing forest, while investing over US$ 260 million into the local communities of the region.[3]

By 2020, Natura seeks to expand its supplier base to include 10,000 families in the Amazon. To help make this a reality, the company is making investments in potential new products and business opportunities that leverage local and traditional knowledge. The desired result is to reduce the deforestation economy in the Amazon and replace it with a profitable "standing forest economy" that includes the sustainable extraction of wood, fruits, and other biodiversity-related products.[4]

Natura is also working to green its supply chain for the sourcing of palm oil. Palm oil is often associated with forest clearing to make way for monoculture, oil-palm plantations. We've seen this happen a lot in Indonesia and Malaysia, which have historically provided nearly 90% of global palm-oil production.[5] Brazil is eager to become a major player in the palm-oil market. Thankfully, the country is exploring alternatives to forest clearing, such as converting degraded cattle pasture land into more lucrative palm-oil plantations.

Since 2007, Natura has partnered with the United States Agency for International Development to develop alternative methods of palm cultivation. Natura began a 44-acre pilot project that replaces palm monoculture with an agroforestry system where oil-palm cultivation is carried out alongside other plant species. The results have been positive so far. The pilot project has yielded more palm oil than the traditional monoculture system while preventing deforestation and providing ecosystem benefits, such as natural pest control and carbon sequestration.[6]

Policies and Procedures

Natura has a wide variety of policies, procedures, and targets in place that help drive innovative, sustainable improvements to process and products. For example, Natura conducts environmental-accounting studies to assess the positive and negative impacts for all stages of the product life cycle, including production, marketing, product use, and final disposal of waste. Environmental impacts, such as land use, water consumption and pollution, solid-waste generation, and greenhouse-gas emissions, are then translated into financial values. Using 2013 data, Natura calculated a total environmental impact of R$ 132 million (using the Brazilian "real" currency).[7] The impact and financial data help Natura identify opportunities for improvement and set new policies, procedures, and performance targets. In July 2016, Natura became the first Latin American company, and the first company in the global cosmetics industry, to publish the full findings of its environmental profit-and-loss assessment.

Here are some of Natura's sustainability-related policies, procedures, and targets for 2020:

- **Carbon-neutral.** Since 2007, Natura has had a policy of being carbon-neutral each year.
- **Packaging.** At least 10% of all Natura Brazil packaging should be made of post-consumer recycled material.
- **Climate change.** By 2020, the Natura brand must reduce its relative emissions of greenhouse gases by 33% compared to 2012 levels. This will be a challenge given that Natura already reduced its relative emissions of greenhouse gases by 33% from 2007 to 2012.
- **Waste.** Collect and recycle 50% of the waste generated (ton-equivalent) by Natura product packaging in Brazil.
- **Water.** Create and implement a strategy to reduce impacts across the entire value chain based on water footprint measurements for the Natura brand in Brazil.
- **Intellectual and genetic property rights.** The regulatory control over intellectual property rights in the Amazon is not clear, so Natura decided to establish individual agreements with each of its approximately 2,500 small suppliers to guard against the unethical commercialization of the region's genetic and cultural heritage. These agreements include commitments to fair compensation as well as technical and social investments.[8]

Carbon-Offset Program

Natura's Carbon Neutral Program includes ongoing measurements of greenhouse gas emissions, efforts to reduce the amount of emissions that are generated from its operations, and the purchase of offsets to cover the remaining balance of emissions that can't be avoided. Thirty-seven percent of the carbon offsets are purchased from forest regeneration and maintenance projects, and the remaining 63% are purchased from projects related to energy efficiency and the substitution of fossil fuels.[9] Natura is the fourth largest global company taking part in the world's voluntary carbon credit market.[10]

In 2016, Natura achieved its goal to locally compensate for emissions in each of the countries that are part of its international operations. At present, 41% of Natura's portfolio of carbon-offset projects take place in the Amazon, preventing 1.16 million tons of carbon dioxide (CO_2) from being emitted into the atmosphere.[11]

Through its carbon-offset purchases, Natura has supported the following forest-restoration and forest-conservation projects:

- **Forest restoration.** Natura has provided funding for 13 forest-restoration projects that restored a total area of 5,325 acres, representing a variety of plant and animal communities in the Amazon, the Atlantic forest, and other biomes. These restoration projects removed 639,933 tons of CO_2e of greenhouse gases from the atmosphere.[12]
- **Forest conservation.** Natura supported five forest-conservation projects that protect a total area of 29,986 acres, primarily in the Amazon. These conservation projects removed 382,602 tons of CO_2e of greenhouse gases from the atmosphere.[13]

Since the beginning of its carbon-offset program, Natura has signed contracts for 35 initiatives in Brazil and other countries in Latin America where it operates. Here are a few examples of the types of carbon-offset projects that Natura supported through the purchase of carbon offsets:

- **Chile.** Acquired 26,600 carbon credits from the Valdiviana Coastal Reserve, a protected area that is managed by The Nature Conservancy.[14]
- **Peru.** Purchased 62,420 carbon credits from Bosques Amazónicos, Peru's largest forest initiative. This was the largest transaction of its kind that had ever occurred in Peru by a private company.[15]
- **Argentina.** Paid US$ 4 million to acquire 70,000 carbon credits from the Rawson wind farm. This was the largest transaction of its kind in Argentina and was the first one that had been carried out voluntarily.[16]
- **Mexico.** Signed a contract to obtain 4,367 credits in exchange for a support of an eco-efficient stove project. This project will reduce emissions by 190,000 tons of CO_2e, and the more efficient stoves will save each family about US$ 10 per month.[17]

Invasive Species

For the second major threat to biodiversity—invasive species—Natura doesn't mention any related activities in its various reports or on their website.

Pollution, Climate Change, and Ocean Acidification

Natura is actively pursuing all four of the strategies that we covered for combating pollution, climate change, and ocean acidification: Design for the Environment (DfE), pollution prevention, green building, and carbon offsets. We won't go into any more detail about Natura's carbon-offset program since we've already covered it.

Design for the Environment

Natura doesn't mention DfE in its reports, but it's clear that sustainable design is an important factor in the company's product-development efforts. Sustainability concerns have influenced changes to many of Natura's formulas. As a result, 83% of the company's ingredients now have a renewable, vegetable-based origin rather than a fossil-based origin.[18] Natura's research team also monitors scientific standards and looks for any controversial ingredients. If evidence suggests that a certain ingredient poses a risk to the environment or human health, then Natura replaces that ingredient in its formulas.

Pollution Prevention

Natura is pursuing a wide variety of pollution-prevention initiatives, often in partnership with its suppliers and consumers. For example, Natura has a 2020 goal to ensure that at least 10% of all Natura Brazil packaging should be made of post-consumer recycled material.[19] To accomplish this, the company looks for opportunities to use materials that have a smaller environmental impact, such as the use of recycled glass in its fragrance bottles. Natura also launched the Ekos line of products, which uses 100% recycled polyethylene terephthalate.[20]

On the consumer end, Natura is encouraging the use of refills and the proper disposal of packaging, and these efforts seem to be paying off. In 2014, 1.2% of all packaging used post-consumer recycled materials; by 2016, that number had increased to 4.3%.[21] Natura will continue to partner with suppliers and consumers in the effort to reach its 10% target by 2020.

Water-use efficiency is another area on which Natura is focusing, and it has proved to be a challenging issue so far. Water-use efficiency has gone in the wrong direction for the past few years, moving from 0.45 liters per unit manufactured in 2014 to 0.53 liters per unit manufactured in 2016.[22] This decrease in water-use efficiency was due in part to reductions in production volumes, which impact the efficiency metric. This measure has also proved to be challenging because Natura uses a cradle-to-grave metric for water-use efficiency. This means that Natura factors in the volume of water used by consumers when taking a shower as well as the heating of that water, since Brazilian electricity is largely based on hydroelectric power. Natura is in the process of conducting studies to identify projects that have the potential to reduce the company's water footprint.

Here are some of the other pollution-prevention activities that Natura is pursuing to reduce its impact to the environment:

- Reduce the use of air shipments for exports to other Latin American operations.
- Use coastal shipping, rather than road transportation, to supply distribution centers in certain parts of Brazil.
- Use electric vehicles to deliver its products to consultants and consumers, making Natura the first company in Latin America to do this. Natura has five electric vehicles in four cities, and these vehicles emit nine times less CO_2 compared with regular vehicles.[23] In the cities of Vitória and Porto Alegre, Natura takes this idea a step further by using bicycles with baggage compartments to deliver products and catalogs to consumers and consultants.
- Reduce electricity consumption at its various sites of operation.
- Optimize production of product catalogs.
- Reduce its relative emissions of greenhouse gases by 33% by 2020 through a variety of pollution-prevention activities.[24]
- Use organic alcohol in 100% of its fragrance products. This organic alcohol is produced without pesticides, chemical fertilizers, or burning. Natura estimates this change has helped restore 49,421 acres of forest, facilitated the return of 340 animal species, including endangered species like jaguars, and increased the volume of water in nearby streams by 30%.[25]

- Switched to a different type of paper that generates fewer air emissions when printing product catalogs.

Green Building

While Natura doesn't mention a formal "green building" program or strategy in its various reports and website, some of the company's efforts may be considered green-building strategies. For example, Natura created an 18.3-million-square-foot industrial complex called Ecoparque, which is designed to be a closed-cycle system that generates no waste while processing Amazonian fruits, oils, and berries for its cosmetics products.

Ecoparque was built with the intention of bringing together a variety of companies from complementary industries that are interested in doing business locally and can potentially use Natura's outputs as their product inputs. Roughly 70% of administrative team employees and 100% of operational team employees at Ecoparque are hired locally.[26] As for the green-building elements at Ecoparque, Natura uses filtration gardens to treat wastewater, uses natural ventilation and lighting where possible, and installed a geothermal system that improves the efficiency of the air-conditioning system.

Overharvesting

Natura address the threat of overharvesting through a variety of "greening the supply chain" activities. We've already touched on this subject, but I've included a few more details below on the topics of responsible harvesting, and supplier scorecards and audits.

Responsible Harvesting

As we've seen throughout this chapter, Natura partners closely with its suppliers to ensure that sustainable practices are used to gather raw ingredients for Natura products. Let's look at the Ekos Ucuuba line of moisturizing products as an example.

The Ekos Ucuuba product line is derived from the fruit of the ucuuba tree—a tall, thin tree that ranges from 16 to 98 feet in height. The seeds of the ucuuba tree contain fatty acids, such as trimyristin, which have excellent moisturizing properties and a light texture. Unfortunately, the ucuuba tree is threatened with extinction because its wood is commonly exploited to make stakes, broom handles, door frames, and roofing.

Natura is trying to reduce this threat by creating a market for nontimber products that are derived from the tree. This creates a financial incentive for the local community to keep the ucuuba tree standing rather than let the trees be cut down unsustainably for timber products. In addition, community members who supply the ucuuba seeds to Natura are instructed to harvest only 50% of the fruit, and let the remainder fall and be carried away to keep the tree's germination process intact.[27]

Another example of responsible harvesting relates to Natura's supply of cocoa. Since 2007, Natura has been working with 120 small cocoa growers along the Transamazônica highway in Southeastern Pará to train them in organic production techniques. Through this partnership, participating farmers can sell cocoa to Natura as well as to several chocolate manufacturers in Europe.[28]

Supplier Scorecards and Audits

Given how much Natura relies on suppliers to acquire raw ingredients using sustainable methods, it's no surprise that the company has a robust supplier-audit program in place. In 2016, 100% of Natura's supplier communities were audited by the company's Socio-biodiversity Chain Verification System. These annual audits ensure that suppliers have a system in place to confirm the origin of all raw materials and are meeting requirements related to labor issues, organization management, and good production practices. Each audit results in the creation of an action plan that is monitored and assessed in the next annual audit. Natura offers to work with any suppliers that need assistance with improving their performance.

Natura also conducts in-person audits to evaluate potential new suppliers. These audits include impartial, objective criteria in the areas of quality, environment, social responsibility, and occupational safety and health. Suppliers that meet the criteria are then required to complete online training related to the Natura Code of Ethics.

Suppliers are also encouraged to produce sustainability reports. These reports are not a requirement for doing business with Natura, and they aren't used as a tool to evaluate supplier performance and compliance. Instead, the sustainability reports are used as a way to engage with suppliers in sustainability and improve understanding of Natura's requirements and culture. The company assesses supplier compliance with policies and procedures through its monitoring and audit programs. The company also provides training and coaching to suppliers that voluntarily agree to generate a report. Each year, Natura recognizes the most noteworthy supplier community by presenting them with a Qlicar Award, which is based on a variety of criteria related to quality and good practices.

Profitable Conservation: Summary

There isn't much in the way of ROI data in Natura's reports or website; however, the company does provide us with a summary of how much money it's investing in various areas related to the environment. Here's a table of environmental investments that Natura published in its 2016 Annual Report:[29]

Annual Investments and Spending on Environmental Protection (R$ thousand)	Details	2014	2015	2016
Socio-biodiversity	Amazon Program	385,000	169,765	220,700
Climate change	Carbon Neutral Program	1,731	764	3,293
Waste	Reverse Logistics Program and disposal of industrial waste from Natura units	6,327	9,935	11,375
Water and effluent	Water Footprint Program and treatment of industrial effluent from Natura units	2,685	3,410	3,583
Innovation and social and environmental technology	Sustainable technology for products and clean technology implemented in operations	6,645	6,661	3,874
Social	Programs such as Natura Movement, HDI-NC and Local Development at Natura units	2,081	2,784	2,225

Annual Investments and Spending on Environmental Protection (R$ thousand)	Details	2014	2015	2016
Others	Support, sponsorship and associations related to sustainability as well as environmental insurance	1,880	1,263	1,194
TOTAL		406,349	194,582	246,244

These numbers are helpful in terms of understanding Natura's environmental priorities, but it doesn't help us determine the financial ROI for the various conservation activities that help protect wildlife and biodiversity. Of course, the mere fact that the company is pursuing these strategies is a good indication that Natura perceives these activities as adding significant value to its business.

Chapter 8 Endnotes

1. Natura, "who we are: press release." September 11, 2017. Accessed June 14, 2018. http://www.natura.com.br/fiquepordentro/group/release.
2. The Body Shop, "Stay in the Know." Forever Against Animal Testing | Cruelty Free. Accessed June 14, 2018. https://www.thebodyshop.com/en-us/commitment/manifesto.
3. Natura Corporation (2016). "Natura 2016 Annual Report," 50.
4. Ibid., 58.
5. K. G. Austin, A. Mosnier, J. Pirker, I. Mccallum, S. Fritz, and P.s. Kasibhatla, "Shifting Patterns of Oil Palm Driven Deforestation in Indonesia and Implications for Zero-deforestation Commitments." Land Use Policy 69 (2017): 41-48. doi:10.1016/j.landusepol.2017.08.036.
6. Note 3, supra, 55.
7. Ibid., 64.
8. Ibid., 60.
9. Ibid., 61.
10. Ibid.

11. Ibid., 60.
12. Ibid., 63.
13. Ibid.
14. Ibid., 61.
15. Ibid.
16. Ibid.
17. Ibid., 62.
18. Ibid., 16.
19. Ibid., 51.
20. Ibid.
21. Ibid., 66.
22. Ibid., 143.
23. Ibid., 62.
24. Ibid., 51.
25. Ibid., 62.
26. Natura Corporation, "Natura B-Corp Impact Assessment," 39. http://www.bcorporation.net/sites/default/files/documents/bcorps/natura/Natura_Transparent_Assessment_public2.pdf.
27. Natura, "A win-win cycle for everyone." June 07, 2016. Accessed June 14, 2018. https://www.natura.com.br/en/annual-report/2015/in-products/a-win-win-cycle-for-everyone.
28. Oliver Balch, "Natura commits to sourcing sustainably from Amazon." The Guardian. March 18, 2013. Accessed June 14, 2018. https://www.theguardian.com/sustainable-business/natura-sourcing-sustainably-from-amazon.
29. Note 3, supra, 149.

CHAPTER 9

Profitable-Conservation Case Study: BHP Billiton (Australia and the United Kingdom)

"BHP Billiton is committed to operating sustainably – it is one of Our Charter values. Improving our management of land, enhancing biodiversity and contributing to enduring benefits is essential to operating in a responsible and sustainable manner."

—Mike Henry, President Operations, Minerals Australia, BHP Billiton

Company Overview

Founded in 1885, BHP Billiton has become one of the largest mining companies in the world. You'll find BHP Billiton listed on both the Australian Securities Exchange and the London Stock Exchange because of a 2001 merger between the Australian Broken Hill Proprietary Company Limited and the Anglo-Dutch Billiton. The two parent companies—BHP Billiton Limited and BHP Billiton Plc—operate as if they're a single entity called BHP, with global headquarters in Melbourne, Australia.

Today, BHP has over 60,000 employees and contractors scattered across the globe in the following divisions:

- **Minerals Australia.** Iron ore, copper, coal, and nickel operations in Western Australia, Queensland, New South Wales, and South Australia.
- **Minerals Americas.** Copper, zinc, iron ore, coal, and potash operations in Canada, Chile, Peru, the United States, Colombia, and Brazil.
- **Petroleum.** Oil and gas exploration, development, and production operations in Australia, the United States, the Gulf of Mexico, Trinidad and Tobago, Algeria, and the United Kingdom.
- **Marketing:** BHP's Marketing group is an interdependent core business of BHP that manages the inward and outward supply chains.

BHP used the Global Reporting Initiative (GRI) Comprehensive level standards as well as the GRI Mining and Metals Sector Disclosures to create its BHP Sustainability Report 2017. The company also published Sustainability Reporting Navigator 2017, which specifies where to find information about specific impacts in the company's Sustainability Report, Annual Report, Economic Contribution Report, and Climate Change: Portfolio Analysis Report.

Companies in the mining and energy-resource development industries have the potential to severely affect local wildlife and biodiversity. When we look at individual mines, the impact may not seem significant compared to some other types of land use. However, the cumulative impact of exploration, development, and mining has the greatest potential to negatively impact wildlife and biodiversity. This can happen through the clearing of land, contamination of soil and water, construction of roads and pipelines, and the diversion of rivers and other water sources to provide water for mining.

Using GRI's guidelines and stakeholder input, BHP created the following list of "material" environmental topics to include in its Sustainability Report:

- Water management and access
- Biodiversity and land management
- Environmental incidents
- Air emissions
- Climate-change policy and portfolio resilience

- Responding to the physical impacts of climate change
- Managing and minimizing greenhouse-gas emissions from its operations and downstream use of its products
- Energy management and security

Since 1997, BHP has been setting global-sustainability targets that help the company focus on its highest priority risks. BHP sets performance targets using a five-year cycle that is based on fiscal year (FY) rather than calendar year. The most recent five-year cycle (FY 2013 to FY 2017) closed in June 2017. In July 2017, BHP launched its latest round of sustainability-performance targets to cover its operations from FY 2018 to FY 2022. Below you'll find a summary of the environmental-performance targets that BHP set for these five-year cycles.

For its FY 2013 to FY 2017 performance-target cycle, BHP met the environment-related targets that it set, which included the following targets and results:

- **Target.** No significant environmental events at BHP's operated assets in FY 2017. A "significant event" is defined as a severity rating of four and above on BHP's internal severity-rating scale, which ranges from 1 to 7.
    - While BHP didn't have a significant event in FY 2017, the company had a massive environmental event in November 2015: the Samarco dam failure, which we'll discuss in the habitat destruction section of this chapter.
- **Target.** All assets with material, water-related risks will set targets and implement projects to reduce their impact on water resources.
    - By the end of FY 2017, all of BHP's assets that had identified material, water-related risks had implemented at least one project to improve the management of their water resources.
- **Target.** All assets will develop dedicated biodiversity-management plans, including controls to prevent, minimize, rehabilitate, and offset impacts to biodiversity.
    - All of BHP's assets had land- and biodiversity-management plans in place by the end of FY 2017.
- **Target.** BHP will finance the conservation and continuing management of areas of high biodiversity and ecosystem value that are of national or international conservation significance.

  - BHP committed over US$ 50 million towards the conservation and continuing management of over 1.5 million acres of high-biodiversity and ecosystem-value land.[1]

- **Target.** For climate change, BHP had set a goal to maintain total greenhouse-gas emissions below FY 2006 levels while continuing to grow its business.

  - By the end of FY 2017, BHP achieved a 21% reduction in its greenhouse-gas emissions compared with the FY 2006 base year, and a reduction of 975,000 tons of CO_2e since FY 2013.[2]

In June 2017, BHP created a new set of environment-related targets for the FY 2018 to FY 2022 cycle:

- BHP will maintain FY 2022 greenhouse-gas emissions at or below FY 2017 levels while BHP continues to grow its business. This includes the possible use of carbon offsets as needed. BHP also set a longer-term goal to achieve net-zero, operational greenhouse-gas emissions in the second half of this century.
- Zero significant environmental events, using the same internal rating scale that was mentioned earlier.
- Reduce FY 2022 fresh water withdrawal by 35% from FY 2017 levels. BHP also set a longer-term goal to collaborate to enable integrated water-resource management in all catchments where it operates by FY 2030.
- Improve marine- and terrestrial-biodiversity outcomes by the following means:

  - Develop a framework to evaluate and verify the benefits of its actions in collaboration with others.
  - Contribute to the management of areas of national or international conservation significance in an amount that exceeds BHP's disturbed-land footprint.

- In the longer term, BHP set a goal to make a measurable contribution to the conservation, restoration, and sustainable use of marine and terrestrial ecosystems in all regions where it operates by FY 2030.

Now that we have a better idea of BHP's environmental impacts, priorities, and targets, let's look at what BHP is doing to specifically address four of the greatest threats to biodiversity and wildlife conservation: habitat destruction; invasive species; pollution, climate change, and ocean acidification; and overharvesting.

Habitat Destruction

When it comes to land and biodiversity impacts, BHP follows an environmental-mitigation hierarchy of "avoid, minimize, rehabilitate, and compensate," which mirrors the strategies that we covered in Chapter 3. To implement this mitigation hierarchy, BHP requires its assets to understand their baseline conditions and consider direct, indirect, and cumulative impacts to the environment. Based on that analysis, BHP prioritizes actions that avoid, minimize, and rehabilitate and restore environmental impacts over time. Voluntary compensatory actions are then used to offset any actual or reasonably foreseeable residual impacts to biodiversity and ecosystems. We'll look at each of these strategies in more detail below.

Avoidance

BHP has various policies in place to avoid, when possible, negative impacts to the environment within the company's area of influence. For example, BHP will not explore or extract resources within the boundaries of World Heritage-listed sites or operate in areas where there's a risk of direct ecosystem impacts that could result in the extinction of a species on the International Union for Conservation of Nature (IUCN) Red List of Threatened Species. BHP also refrains from exploring or extracting resources within, or adjacent to, the boundaries of IUCN Protected Area Categories I to IV unless the company has a plan in place that meets regulatory requirements, considers stakeholder expectations, and contributes to the values for which the protected area is listed.

Minimization

When avoidance is not possible, BHP requires its assets to minimize the severity of environmental impacts by using systems and controls that help the company achieve its environmental-performance targets. Unfortunately, these minimization systems and controls aren't always effective as we'll see in the example below.

In November 2015, there was a tragic failure of the Samarco dam in Brazil, a 50 / 50 joint venture between BHP Billiton Brasil (nonoperating role) and Vale S.A., a Brazilian mining company. The Samarco dam failure killed 19 people and released 60 million cubic meters of iron-ore waste, which flooded several communities and made them unlivable, and caused significant damage to the environment of the Rio Doce basin. The dam's collapse was attributed to construction and design flaws.[3]

The operator of the Samarco dam—Vale S.A.—had already received plenty of negative press in the environmental community prior to the tragedy. Vale even won an undesirable 2012 Public Eye Award from Greenpeace Switzerland and the Berne Declaration for being the corporation with the most "contempt for the environment and human rights" in the world.[4] This recognition was largely due to Vale's role as a private investor to help fund the controversial Belo Monte dam in the Amazon rainforest of Brazil.

The Samarco dam failure had a major financial impact on BHP. In August 2016, BHP recorded its worst annual loss in history—US$ 6.4 billion, which can be attributed in part to Samarco.[5]

In response to the dam failure, BHP has implemented a wide variety of initiatives to improve its policies and procedures and to rehabilitate and restore impacted land and communities. For starters, BHP created a centralized leadership and support team as well as global standards for all of BHP's nonoperated joint ventures. These global standards include a requirement for its nonoperated joint-venture partners to identify and manage risks, and implement communication strategies and audits, to help ensure compliance with BHP's standards.

BHP also created requirements for its assets to develop closure plans that include potentially significant financial, environmental, and social risks associated with future closure of its operations. These closure plans are included in BHP's planning and decision-making processes and are subject to internal audits to assess their effectiveness. In FY 2018, BHP will continue to develop and implement standards for how BHP interacts with its nonoperated joint ventures based on best practices in governance and assurance.

Following Samarco, BHP completed risk reviews for all significant dams and confirmed that these other dams were stable. BHP is now focused on risk identification, governance, and monitoring programs to ensure that the company's tailing dams are receiving continuous monitoring and maintenance. Priorities for FY 2018 include the implementation of a stewardship program, monitoring and early-warning technologies, emergency-response preparedness, and the development of additional controls and standards for BHP's dams and tailings.

Rehabilitation and Restoration

BHP assets are required to implement rehabilitation plans that take into consideration both regulatory requirements and stakeholder expectations. These plans include the need to rehabilitate disturbed areas that are no longer required for operational purposes.

When it comes to Samarco, the requirements and expectations for restoration and rehabilitation are understandably huge. After the initial emergency-response phase, BHP Billiton Brasil and Vale established a private, nonprofit foundation called Fundação Renova to restore the environment and rebuild communities. The IUCN oversees an independent scientific, technical, and advisory panel to guide the foundation's restoration activities. Fundação Renova's now has over 400 staff and 2,500 contractors, with a CY 2017 budget of R$ 1.94 billion (US$ 590 million).[6]

One of the foundation's first steps was to complete geochemical analyses to assess the toxicity of the mine tailings. The analysis concluded that the tailings material is nontoxic and does not pose a risk to human health.[7] Additional studies are being performed to see if the tailings are causing excessive amounts of metals in fish. There's a precautionary fishing ban in place while these studies are being conducted.

Another early area of focus for Fundação Renova was erosion stabilization. High-priority areas were revegetated with quick-growing species of plants to help reduce erosion risks while longer-term measures are developed and implemented. The foundation plans to rehabilitate nearly 100,000 acres of degraded land, based on consultations with experts, regulatory agencies, and the local community. BHP has revegetated 500 degraded natural springs and has committed to rehabilitating an additional 4,500 springs over the next 10 years.[8] The company is also working to build additional retention structures to contain tailings during the wet season.

In 2016, Samarco, Vale, and BHP agreed to a deal to pay up to $US 2.3 billion over the course of six years for restoration work and compensation.[9]

Biodiversity Offsets and Voluntary Compensatory Actions

BHP doesn't appear to have a formal biodiversity-offset program that links offsets to the biodiversity impacts of specific development projects. Instead, the company sets voluntary targets to finance the conservation and ongoing management of areas of high-biodiversity and ecosystem value that are of national or international conservation significance. Some of these projects serve a dual purpose of meeting biodiversity and ecosystem-conservation goals while also providing BHP with carbon credits for reducing greenhouse-gas emissions.

BHP has partnered with nonprofit organization Conservation International to identify conservation opportunities and improve its approach to biodiversity management. By the end of FY 2017, BHP had committed over US$ 50 million to support conservation projects.[10] Here are a few examples:

- **Five Rivers Conservation Project in Tasmania, Australia.** This multiyear project was launched in 2014 in partnership with the Tasmanian Land Conservancy and Conservation International. The US$ 10.5 million-effort supports conservation and ongoing management for 27,182 acres of land in Tasmania. The land includes old-growth forests, rivers, and alpine wetlands, and is home to endangered species, such as the Tasmanian devil and the Tasmanian wedge-tailed eagle. Project funding includes an endowment for long-term management of the land.
- **Valdivian Coastal Reserve in Chile.** BHP Billiton partnered with Conservation International and The Nature Conservancy to permanently conserve roughly 125,000 acres of temperate rainforest of the Valdivian Coastal Reserve in the Los Rios region of Chile. This effort included the largest restoration of native forest in Chile through the removal of 8,649 acres of nonnative eucalyptus trees and the planting of more than 2.5 million native trees. The reserve is included on the World Wildlife Fund's Global 200 list as one of "Earth's terrestrial, freshwater and marine ecosystems that harbor exceptional biodiversity," and it's also one of 34 biodiversity hotspots identified by Conservation International.[11] The agreement included a conservation easement to ensure that future uses of the Valdivian Coastal Reserve are focused on conservation. Local com-

munities are also expected to benefit from ecotourism, crafts, and other entrepreneurial opportunities.

- **Raine Island Recovery Project in Queensland, Australia.** Raine Island is the breeding ground for one of the world's largest populations of green turtles and serves as the most important seabird rookery in the Great Barrier Reef World Heritage Area. As many as 60,000 female green turtles swim from their feeding grounds in Indonesia, Papua New Guinea, the Torres Strait, and the West Pacific to lay their eggs on Raine Island. Green-turtle populations are in danger due to a combination of factors, such as changes in the island's landscape, habitat loss, boat strikes, overharvesting, and pollution. These changes in the island's landscape have caused tidal inundation, which kills newly laid eggs that can't survive underwater, and the death of approximately 2,000 adult turtles from overturning and entrapment.[12] The Raine Island Recovery Project is restoring a turtle-nesting habitat through reprofiling of the beach, installing cliff-top fencing to reduce mortality of nesting female turtles, rescuing stranded and overturned nesting female turtles, monitoring key island species, and building indigenous ranger capacity. To help keep this turtle and bird sanctuary intact, BHP collaborated with the Queensland government, the Great Barrier Reef Marine Park Authority, Wuthathi and Kemer Kemer Meriam Nation Traditional Owners, and the Great Barrier Reef Foundation on this AUD$ 7.95-million project.[13]
- **Alto Mayo Protected Forest in Peru.** In partnership with Conservation International Peru and other corporate donors, such as Disney, this two-year, US$ 5-million project aims to address the main causes of deforestation by providing alternative livelihood opportunities, such as sustainable coffee growing and enhanced forest governance. So far, 848 families have received agricultural training, educational materials, and medical supplies in exchange for pledging not to cut down trees in the Alto Mayo. The training and educational programs have yielded higher incomes and improved productivity for participating families.[14] This project is part of the REDD+ initiative that was created under the UN Framework Convention on Climate Change to reduce greenhouse gas emissions by creating incentives to protect and restore forests. REDD+ stands for "reducing emis-

sions from deforestation and forest degradation, plus the role of conservation, sustainable management of forests, and the enhancement of forest carbon stocks."[15] BHP received 800,000 tons of carbon credits in exchange for its support for the Alto Mayo initiative in Peru.

- **Kasigau Corridor REDD Project in Kenya.** BHP contributed to a Forest Bond that was issued by the International Finance Corporation, which provides BHP with carbon credits that are generated from the avoidance of deforestation through projects like the Kasigau Corridor REDD Project. The Wildlife Works' Kasigau Corridor REDD Project created a sanctuary for wildlife and flora while providing an income to the local community for protecting the land in a region that previously relied on deforestation.

Overall, these investments helped conserve over 1.5 million acres of land, improve the livelihoods of roughly 2,500 people through conservation agreements, and continue to provide drinking water for over 250,000 people.[16]

Invasive Species

The topic of invasive species isn't covered in BHP's Annual Report or website. The only mention of the topic is related to the Valdivian Coastal Reserve project in Chile, which included the removal of 8,649 acres of nonnative eucalyptus trees.

Pollution, Climate Change, and Ocean Acidification

When it comes to the topic of pollution, BHP's primary emphasis is on water management and greenhouse-gas emissions. This is in addition to normal compliance-related activities, such as the management of stormwater, air emissions, and hazardous materials. BHP has also been active in pursuing Leadership in Energy and Environmental Design (LEED) certifications for many of its buildings. As a result, this section will focus on BHP's efforts in the areas of water management, green building, and climate change.

Water Management

For the past five years, BHP has been working with its assets that identified water as a material risk to help them implement at least one project to improve how they manage their water resources. Over the next five years, BHP's goal is to reduce FY 2022 freshwater withdrawal by 15% from FY 2017 levels. To accomplish this goal, BHP is using recycled water or lower-quality water, where appropriate, in its extraction operations. In FY 2017, BHP's total water input was 283,900 megaliters (nearly 75 billion gallons), where 91% of the water input was classified as Type 2 (suitable for some purposes) or Type 3 (unsuitable for most purposes).[17]

BHP has also set a longer-term goal to enable integrated water-resource management at all catchments where it operates by FY 2030. It's a bit unclear what this goal really means in practice. "Integrated water-resource management" typically refers to processes that promote the coordinated development and management of water, land, and other resources in a way that creates benefits to the economy and society without harming vital ecosystems. "Catchments" are areas where water is collected by the natural landscape and flows into a creek, a river, a dam, a lake, an ocean, or a groundwater system. Putting all of this together, we can rephrase BHP's goal to say that BHP will be developing regional water-management processes to ensure that water is managed in a sustainable manner, considering local water availability, water quality, landscape, climate, and the water needs of impacted communities and ecosystems.

As an example of this type of approach, BHP recently completed a major water project in Chile where it constructed a desalination plant and a 112-mile, water-transport system to provide water for its Escondida copper mine. The plant was constructed at a cost of US$ 3.4 billion and is one of the largest desalination plants in the world. BHP's Kelar natural, gas-fired power plant provides energy to desalinate and pump the water to the mine. Global Water Intelligence awarded the project Industrial Desalination Plant of the Year in recognition for the facility's size and technical complexity. The desalination plant will serve as a sustainable water supply for the Escondida mine and will help reduce pressure on the region's aquifers.[18]

Green Building

BHP has been active in green building over the years, with a LEED Silver building in Chile, LEED Gold buildings in Singapore and Shanghai, and a LEED Platinum certification for its global headquarters building in Melbourne, Australia. These buildings were designed with an emphasis on energy efficiency and carbon-emission reduction. For example, BHP's facility in Perth used 5,680 gallons of low volatile organic compound (VOC) sealants and adhesives, 12,881 gallons of low-VOC paint, and all the wood in the building is recycled from a timber mill in Western Australia.[19] BHP is now pursuing efforts to further reduce the use of energy and water at its various locations.

Climate Change

BHP's climate-change targets for FY 2018 to FY 2022 include maintaining greenhouse-gas emissions at or below FY 2017 levels while growing their business, and achieving net-zero, operational greenhouse-gas emissions in the second half of this century. To accomplish these targets, BHP has adopted four climate-change strategies: mitigation, adaptation, low-emissions technology, and portfolio evaluation. A description of each of these strategies follows.

1. Mitigation efforts include a variety of projects to reduce greenhouse-gas emissions by reducing the company's use of electricity, fuel, and methane. As we saw earlier in this chapter, BHP also uses carbon offsets to reduce the company's overall greenhouse-gas-emissions footprint.
2. BHP's adaptation strategy refers to the company's requirement that each of its assets create a climate-resilience plan that includes climate-change forecasts and mitigation activities for each location. As part of this business-resilience planning, BHP also looks for opportunities to help local communities and ecosystems adapt to climate change.
3. BHP is investing in the rapid development of technologies that will reduce global emissions, such as carbon capture and storage technologies that will reduce fugitive emissions from coal and petroleum operations. In April 2017, BHP collaborated with the University of Melbourne, Stanford University, and Cambridge University to support research in the long-term storage mechanisms of CO_2 in

subsurface locations. The company is also investing in renewable energy battery storage, transportation technologies, and high-efficiency, low-emissions power generation. For example, in Queensland, Australia, BHP is participating in a Lakeland Solar and Storage Project to evaluate the integration of renewable energy sources into its operations.

4. BHP's portfolio evaluation looks at a variety of technical, economic, and political trends to develop scenarios that help the company identify and mitigate possible risks and opportunities. BHP also works with governments, nongovernment organizations, and other stakeholders to create a long-term policy framework that will enable the company to grow while reducing greenhouse-gas emissions.

Because of these four strategies, BHP reduced its emissions of carbon-dioxide equivalent by 21% from FY 2006 to FY 2017 and saved over 975,000 tons of CO_2e from FY 2013 to FY 2017.[20]

Overharvesting

BHP addresses the biodiversity threat of overharvesting through a variety of supply-chain initiatives aimed at raw materials, indirect and direct materials, and labor. Suppliers are prohibited from sourcing any materials from World Heritage-listed sites or IUCN protected areas. In addition, biofuels must be sourced from global companies that have policies or standards for the sustainable sourcing of biofuel components. As one of the largest global shippers of bulk commodities, BHP also conducts risk-based screening of its transportation providers to ensure compliance with BHP's sustainability practices.

BHP uses a risk-based approach for assessing its suppliers where high-risk suppliers are audited to ensure compliance with applicable environmental regulations, permits, and reports as well as the values and ethical practices specified in BHP's Charter, Code of Business Conduct, and Requirements for Supply. The company is in the process of designing and implementing a new category-management platform that will improve its ability to monitor and track supplier performance.

Suppliers receive BHP assistance, as needed, to help them meet BHP's standards and to encourage them to adopt the International Council of Mining and Metals' Sustainable Development Framework. This includes assistance with sustainable design, use, recycling, and disposal practices throughout BHP's product-value chain.

Profitable-Conservation Summary

BHP doesn't provide much in the way of return on environmental-investment data in its various reports or website. Instead, BHP provides data on how much it spends for various initiatives. Here are some examples:

- BHP has committed more than US$ 50 million towards the conservation and continuing management of over 1.5 million acres of high-biodiversity and ecosystem-value land. This is in addition to money spent for ongoing environmental-management activities at each of its sites.[21]
- In response to the Samarco dam failure, Samarco, Vale, and BHP agreed to a deal to pay up to $US 2.3 billion over the course of six years for restoration work and compensation. BHP's Fundação Renova's budget for CY 2017 was US$ 590 million.[22] There are still pending claims against BHP that may result in the establishment of a multibillion-dollar fund that will support future reparation, compensation, and cleanup costs.
- Since 2001, BHP has invested over US$ 2.3 billion to support community programs and other social investments. Each year, BHP contributes 1% of the average of the previous three years' pre-tax profit to these social investments. The social investment in FY 2017 totaled US$ 80.1 million, with US$ 75.1 million allocated towards community-development programs and associated administrative costs, and US$ 5 million allocated to the BHP Billiton Foundation.[23]
- In FY 2017, BHP paid US$ 13.6 billion to its 10,000+ suppliers around the world. Of this amount, US$ 3.0 billion (22%) was paid to local suppliers to help support their development.[24]
- In FY 2017, BHP spent US$ 10.5 million on various investments that provide environmental and social benefits through biodiversity conservation, water stewardship, and climate-change mitigation and adaptation.[25]

- BHP provided a US$ 14-million donation to The Nature Conservancy to support the Sustainable Rivers and Forests Initiative, which has led to the protection of nearly 3,700 acres of critical riverfront property and forestland of Texas and Arkansas.[26]
- In FY 2017, BHP provided US$ 12 million to support an investment bond that is designed to reduce deforestation and stimulate investment in low-carbon development. The Forests Bond was issued by The International Finance Corporation, and it raised US$ 152 million from institutional investors. The bond is intended to support REDD+ projects that demonstrate the value of reducing deforestation as one of the most cost-effective, climate-change solutions.[27]
- BHP contributed $US 2.0 billion out of the US$ 3.4 billion needed to build a desalination plant and water-transport system to support its 57.5% ownership of the Escondida copper mine.[28]
- BHP spent US$ 49 million in FY 2017 to conduct National Environmental Policy Act studies and community-engagement activities for the Resolution Copper project in Arizona. The US$ 49 million represents BHP's 45% interest in the proposed project; Rio Tinto contributed the other 55%. The draft version of the environmental impact study is expected to be made available for public comment in May 2019.[29]

Unfortunately, these numbers don't help us evaluate the financial return on investment for BHP's biodiversity and wildlife conservation-related activities. In addition, the Samarco dam failure is a major driver behind much of BHP's recent environmental spending. However, the company's spending and strategic priorities provide a good indication of the environmental investments that BHP believes add significant value to biodiversity, wildlife, and its business.

Chapter 9 Endnotes

1. BHP, "BHP Sustainability Report 2017," 10.
2. Ibid., 33.
3. BBC News, "Samarco dam failure in Brazil 'caused by design flaws.'" August 30, 2016. Accessed June 15, 2018. https://www.bbc.com/news/business-37218145.

4. Saabira Chaudhuri, "Public Eye award singles out mining company Vale." The Guardian. January 27, 2012. Accessed June 15, 2018. https://www.theguardian.com/environment/2012/jan/27/public-eye-awards-vale-barclays.

5. Note 1, supra, 12.

6. Ibid.

7. Ibid., 13.

8. Ibid.

9. Seeking Alpha, "SEC Form 20-F, BHP Billiton plc." September 21, 2016. https://seekingalpha.com/filing/3230703.

10. Note 1, supra, 37.

11. BHP Billiton, "Valdivian Coastal Reserve." June 21, 2013. Accessed June 15, 2018. https://www.bhp.com/community/community-news/2013/06/valdivian-coastal-reserve.

12. Queensland Government, "Raine Island Recovery Project." Department of National Parks, Sport and Racing. Accessed June 15, 2018. https://www.npsr.qld.gov.au/raineisland/.

13. Ibid.

14. Conservation International, "Implementing Forest Conservation in Peru's Alto Mayo Region." Accessed June 15, 2018. https://www.conservation.org/stories/alto-mayo-protected-forest/Pages/overview.aspx.

15. Ibid.

16. Note 1, supra, 37.

17. Ibid.

18. Ibid., 38.

19. The Fifth Estate, "BHP Billiton receives WA's first 6 Star Green Star Interiors rating." October 17, 2013. Accessed June 15, 2018. https://www.thefifthestate.com.au/articles/bhp-billiton-receive-was-first-6-star-green-star-interiors-rating.

20. Note 1, supra, 10.

21. Ibid.

22. Ibid., 12.

23. Ibid., 25.

24. Ibid.

25. Ibid., 26.

26. Ibid.

27. Ibid., 33.

28. Ibid., 5, 38.

29. U.S. Department of Agriculture, "EIS Status Graphic." Background | Resolution Copper Project and Land Exchange Environmental Impact Statement, March 1, 2018. Accessed June 15, 2018. www.resolutionmineeis.us/documents/usfs-tonto-nepa-process-status-20180314.

CHAPTER 10

Profitable-Conservation Case Study: Walmart (United States)

"The doubters got on board quickly when they saw that our P & L could benefit while we were doing good work for the environment. A constant theme for us in engaging our associates and stakeholders has been shared value: the need to integrate sustainability into business, not treat it as a separate effort, and to ensure we deliver business value as well as value for the environment and society."

—Doug McMillon, CEO of Walmart

Company Overview

With 260 million weekly customers, it's a safe bet that most of us have been to Walmart at one time or another. Walmart is the largest company in the world, with US$ 486 billion in total revenue, and a staggering 2.3 million associates spread across 11,700 stores in 28 countries. There are 1.5 million Walmart employees in the United States alone.[1] The Walmart brand includes Walmart Supercenters, Walmart Neighborhood Markets, Sam's Club (United States, Mexico, Brazil, and China), ASDA (England), and Seiyu (Japan).

When you hear the name "Walmart," it may conjure up all kinds of thoughts, emotions, and images of unflattering customer photos from forwarded emails. But I'm guessing that "natural-resource conservation" was not the first thing that popped into your head. If it did, well, that's odd ... but you'd be right! Walmart is doing noteworthy work on the natural-resource and sustainability front, and this chapter will highlight some of the company's efforts that are specific to biodiversity and wildlife conservation.

For sustainability reporting, Walmart uses the Global Reporting Initiative framework. To identify the priorities and topics on which to focus in its 2017 Global Responsibility Report, Walmart engaged with a wide variety of stakeholders, including customers, employees, suppliers, advisory councils, community leaders, investors, nongovernmental organizations, and government leaders. The data were captured through interviews, working sessions, and survey feedback from 1,750 respondents. This stakeholder feedback identified the following environmental issues of concern and described how Walmart can help address those issues:

- **Climate.** Walmart can address climate change by working to reduce energy intensity, adopt renewable energy, and reduce emissions within the company's operations and supply chain.
- **Natural resources.** This category included deforestation, water quality and quantity, land use, soil health, fish stocks, and biodiversity. Stakeholders suggested that Walmart collaborate with suppliers and others to identify opportunities to decrease impacts to natural resources.
- **Waste.** Walmart can take steps to eliminate waste in its own operations and work to develop "closed-loop" systems throughout production and consumption.
- **Animal welfare.** Walmart can encourage its suppliers to promote responsible antibiotic use and adhere to the "five freedoms" of food production: (1) freedom from hunger and thirst; (2) freedom from discomfort; (3) freedom from pain, injury, or disease; (4) freedom to express normal behavior; and (5) freedom from fear and distress.

In this chapter, I'll focus on Walmart's sustainability efforts to combat the biodiversity threats of habitat destruction; invasive species; pollution, climate change, and ocean acidification; and overharvesting. I've also included return on investment (ROI) data that the company disclosed in its various reports and on its website.

Habitat Destruction

Walmart's primary response to the biodiversity threat of habitat destruction includes the use of voluntary compensatory actions through its Acres for America program and the adoption of a goal to achieve zero-net deforestation. Some of the Acres for America projects that have been implemented include wildlife corridors. Walmart has also been active in the construction of green roofs, although this strategy has been pursued primarily from an energy-efficiency perspective. We'll look at each of these strategies in more detail below.

Voluntary Compensatory Actions: Acres for America

In 2005, Walmart partnered with the National Fish and Wildlife Foundation (NFWF) to establish the Acres for America program "to conserve lands of national significance, protect critical fish and wildlife habitat, and benefit people and local economies."[2]

Acres for America supports biodiversity and natural-resource conservation through four program priorities:

1. Conserve critical habitats for birds, fish, plants, and wildlife.
2. Connect existing protected lands to unify wild places and protect migration routes.
3. Provide access for people to enjoy the outdoors.
4. Support local economies that depend on forestry, ranching, and wildlife.

The result has been impressive. Walmart started with a goal to conserve 1 acre of wildlife habitat for every acre of land developed by Walmart stores but has ended closer to a 10:1 ratio of conservation to development. As of 2017, the program has invested US$ 38.5 million and leveraged more than US$ 376 million in matching contributions to protect 1.2 million acres though 72 projects in 35 states, the District of Columbia, and Puerto Rico.[3]

The Acres for America program has connected over 10 million acres of protected lands to support landscape-scale conservation and wildlife migration, restore urban lands and habitats, and connect youth to the outdoors by investing in community-based projects in many major U.S. cities. Walmart and NFWF renewed this partnership in November 2015, with a new goal to conserve 2 million acres by 2025.[4]

In FY 2017, Acres for America issued six grants, ranging from US$ 225,000 to US$ 1 million to protect 97,000 acres of wildlife habitat as well as several watersheds, watercourses, and wetlands.[5] One of the six grants was used to connect state forests and conservation lands in Pennsylvania. The other five grants were used to support the following projects:

- **Create a wildlife corridor in California that connects wilderness areas, state parks, and national parks, and protects a watershed.** This project was funded through a US$ 500,000 grant to Western Rivers Conservancy, along with $14.7 million in matching contributions, to acquire 47,097 acres of land. This includes the protection of an entire watershed in Del Norte County, which covers 30 miles of Blue Creek and the Klamath River and over 40 miles of additional tributary streams. The effort also involved setting up a partnership with California's largest Native American tribe to create a cold-water sanctuary—critical for the survival of Coho and Chinook salmon—and establish a sustainable community forest to help revitalize the economy of the Yurok people.[6]
- **Preserve native grasslands in Arizona.** A grant of US$ 225,000 was provided to The Trust for Public Land to help generate US$ 3.1 million in matching contributions to permanently protect 16,500 acres of high-quality, native grasslands and a wildlife habitat at the Cienega Grassland Ranch, located near the base of the Chiricahua Mountains in the Sky Island Region of southeastern Arizona. The project also established conservation easements that will allow working-cattle operations to be maintained in the face of increasing pressure for residential development, fragmentation, and conversion to intensive agriculture. The easements will serve to protect an important conservation corridor for desert and grassland bird species.[7]

- **Protect hardwood forests in Tennessee.** A grant of US$ 500,000 was leveraged by The Conservation Fund to generate US$ 6.5 million in matching contributions to protect 14,600 acres of working hardwood forestland in Skinner Mountain Forest in Tennessee's Cumberland Plateau. This includes the protection of critical karst habitat for seven bat species of Greatest Conservation Need. Three of these bat species—the Indiana bat, the gray bat, and the northern long-eared bat—are listed under the Endangered Species Act. The goal of this conservation project is to preserve important ecological sites, increase land connectivity, sustain forestry jobs, create new public-recreation opportunities, and preserve water quality and forest health.[8]
- **Acquire land for the Grand Teton National Park in Wyoming.** A US$ 1 million grant was used by the Grand Teton National Park Foundation to raise an additional US$ 45.2 million in matching contributions to add 640-acre Antelope Flats to Grand Teton National Park and protect the parcel in perpetuity. Antelope Flats had been identified as the highest national-priority acquisition for the U.S. National Park Service because the land serves as a critical migration route for elk, pronghorn, moose, bison, and wolves.[9]
- **Conserve threatened wetlands in Louisiana.** A US$ 380,000 grant helped The Trust for Public Land generate an additional US$ 2 million in matching contributions from the North American Wetlands Conservation Act grant program to protect the 3,476-acre Fleming Plantation by adding it to the Jean Lafitte National Historical Park and Preserve. The site is in the biological hotspot of the Barataria Basin, and it provides a forest, a marsh, and an aquatic habitat for migratory birds, fish, and other wetland-dependent wildlife. The site improves the ecological integrity of the Louisiana gulf coast while providing public-recreation opportunities.[10]

Operational Policies and Procedures: Moving towards Zero-Net Deforestation

A second important policy that Walmart has adopted is the goal to achieve zero-net deforestation by 2020. The company also signed the New York Declaration on Forests, which aims to achieve a 50% reduction in the rate of forest loss by

2020.[11] To determine how to achieve these goals, Walmart first reviewed studies and learned that certain agricultural commodities, such as palm oil, soy, cattle, and timber, were driving most deforestation in the world, so that is where the company decided to focus its attention.

Here is a high-level overview of how Walmart is addressing the major drivers of deforestation in its operations and supply chain:

- **Palm oil.** In 2010, Walmart set a goal to sustainably source any palm oil that is used in its global private-brand products. By the end of 2015, 100% of Walmart's private-brand palm oil was sourced sustainably in accordance with the certification standards of the Roundtable on Sustainable Palm Oil. The company also encourages its national-brand suppliers to source palm oil from sustainable sources. Walmart is now looking for ways to move towards sources of certified, sustainable palm oil that have been physically verified. The company is also determining how it can best support an industry-wide movement as the industry transitions to 100% traceability for sources of palm oil.[12]
- **Beef.** In 2016, Walmart achieved its goal to only source "sustainable beef" that is not associated with deforestation of the Amazon rainforest by getting 100% of its Brazilian beef suppliers to participate in Walmart's Beef Risk Monitoring System. To monitor its supply of beef, Walmart created a geospatial monitoring system that tracks suppliers, volumes, and over 75,000 registered farm locations, and the data are combined with maps that show where deforestation is taking place. The tool then analyzes Walmart orders to ensure that no beef comes from deforested areas. Beef suppliers are trained to manage geographical information at their slaughterhouses and input the coordinates of their suppliers' farms into the system. The company is now working to expand the program to include cow-calf operations to address the risk that cattle might be traded from high-risk ranches to approved ranches, and the risk that ranchers who contribute to deforestation may reregister their operations under different names. As the program expands, other sensitive biomes outside of the Amazon will be included, such as the Cerrado tropical savanna ecoregion of Brazil.[13]

- **Soy.** Walmart is working with its supply chain and the Consumer Goods Forum to acquire soy through deforestation-free channels. Walmart supports an indefinite extension for the Soy Moratorium in the Amazon region of Brazil, which has helped reduce the amount of Brazilian soy that comes from deforested areas from 30% to 1%. The company also supports the expansion of the Soy Moratorium to other parts of Brazil where a similar approach is needed.[14]
- **Pulp and paper products.** To address deforestation through logging for timber, Walmart is working to reduce packaging materials and ensure that pulp and paper products are purchased from sustainable sources. The company set a goal of zero-net deforestation associated with its private brand products and is encouraging its national-brand suppliers to set similar goals. Walmart uses a Sustainability Index to measure and track supplier performance based on the percentage of virgin fiber.[15] We'll be exploring the Sustainability Index in more detail in the Overharvesting section of this chapter.

Green Roofs

Walmart performed some great analyses on the viability of green roofs for its buildings. This included a three-year study, completed in the fall of 2009, on a research roof that Walmart built on one of its Chicago stores. The roof is 133,000 square feet, with 56% vegetated with varieties of sedum planted in 3 inches of soil, and 46% consisting of a standard, white, polyvinyl chloride (PVC) cool roof.[16]

The roof was instrumented to collect a variety of data, such as general weather variables (air temperature, solar radiation, and wind speed / direction), temperature and heat flux through the roof assembly, stormwater-runoff quantity, and basic air-quality parameters like mold and pollen. Stormwater-runoff samples were also collected and sent for water-quality analysis throughout the monitoring period. The company combined this data with policy analyses and cost-benefit analyses to determine if it made more sense to install a green roof or a PVC cool roof for nine Walmart locations scattered across the United States.

Here are the key findings of the study. The lists of data aren't exactly riveting, but there are some interesting results to consider:

- **Stormwater** (based on 100+ precipitation events that occurred during the three-year study)
    - The green roof retained 80% to 90% of small (<1 inches) summer storms and 60% of the largest storm (5.81 inches). This high level of storage capacity per square foot is likely due to the large roof size and the water-retention layer design.[17]
    - The lag time to peak green-roof runoff ranged from 3.25 hours to 1.25 hours, compared with the white roof lag time of less than 15 minutes.[18]
    - The peak-runoff rate from the green roof was 50% to 85% lower than the precipitation-peak rate. The average runoff peak from the green roof was 35% lower than the rainfall peak.[19]
- **Energy**
    - The study calculated an energy savings of 2.2% for a full green roof in Chicago. For locations in other U.S. areas and climates, the energy savings varied from 1% to 6%.[20]
    - The energy savings from a green roof are greater in cold weather than in warm weather, compared with a standard white roof.[21]
    - The green roof reduces peak heat load compared to the white roof, but the overall impact of the green roof on summer-heat flux is like the white roof.[22]
    - The green roof's membrane temperatures are reduced by up to 40 degrees during hot weather, compared with a standard white roof.[23]
    - Overall, the green roof yielded a 6% to 11% reduction in heating energy and a 7% to 15% reduction in cooling energy. This translates to a 2% to 6% savings in total modeled store energy use (kWh), which would result in US$ 6,000 to US$ 18,000 annual savings for a full green roof.[24]
- **Financial**
    - Green roofs have less than a 20-year payback for each of the nine locations studied. Three of the locations had a payback of zero to three years.[25]

- The cost to install a green roof is roughly US$ 11.50 per square foot more than a traditional white roof.[26]
- Green roofs provide cost savings in the form of rebates, tax and permitting incentives, reduced need for stormwater infrastructure, fewer roof repairs, energy savings, and roof-membrane longevity.
- Depending on location, the 40-year, net-present value of green roofs ranged from US$ 1.8 million to –US$ 0.6 million, with an internal rate of return of 4% to 36%.[27]
- Green roofs have significant community benefits that aren't considered in cost-benefit calculations. These intangible benefits include heat-island reduction, a habitat to support biodiversity, and aesthetics. Locations that offer incentives in exchange for these and other benefits offered the best ROI for Walmart.
- Green roofs roughly double the life of the roof's waterproof membrane by protecting it from wear and tear.
- The green roof was estimated to have a maintenance savings of US$ 0.05 per square foot per year compared to the white roof due to the protection that the green roof provides to the membrane and drains, preventing damage and clogging.[28]
- Large green roofs appear to perform better than small roofs on a per-square-foot basis.

Overall, Walmart concluded that, compared with a standard white roof, green roofs are a worthwhile investment in some but not all locations. As a result, Walmart performs analyses for any city in which a new Walmart store is built to determine if it makes sense to install a green roof. In some locations, Walmart moves forward with a green roof; in others, it installs a standard white roof. In most cities, local stormwater regulations and incentives are the most significant factor that influences the cost-effectiveness of green roofs.

Invasive Species

Our second major threat to biodiversity—invasive species—is not addressed in Walmart's reports or on their website. However, I did learn that in Hawaii, Walmart has agreed to refrain from selling two plant species (night-blooming jasmine and medinilla) from its garden centers due to concerns that these plants could become a damaging invasive species in the state.

Pollution, Climate Change, and Ocean Acidification

When it comes to pollution, climate-change, and ocean-acidification threats to biodiversity and wildlife, Walmart focuses its attention on pollution prevention and Design for the Environment. Walmart has two primary goals in this area: reduce energy intensity and emissions and eliminate waste in its operations.

Reducing Energy Intensity and Emissions

Walmart was the first retailer to create an emissions-reduction plan that was approved by the Science Based Targets initiative. The Science Based Targets initiative is a partnership among the Carbon Disclosure Project, the United Nations Global Compact, the World Resources Institute, and the World Wildlife Fund to help companies determine how much to cut emissions in the effort to prevent the worst impacts of climate change.

In October 2016, Walmart created the following goals as part of its emission-reduction plan:

- Reduce emissions in its own operations by 18% by 2025, using 2015 levels as a baseline.[29]
- Work with suppliers to achieve a 1-gigaton reduction in emissions generated from the production and use of products that Walmart sells between 2015 and 2030. This huge reduction in emissions is roughly three times the size of California's annual emissions.[30]

To accomplish these two goals, Walmart is implementing four core strategies: scaling clean, affordable, renewable energy; improving energy efficiency; improving facility refrigeration systems; and maximizing trucking-fleet efficiency.

Scaling Clean, Affordable, Renewable Energy

Walmart has set a goal to be powered by 50% renewable energy by 2025, with a longer-term goal of operating with 100% renewable energy.[31] To meet these goals, Walmart is installing renewable-energy technologies at many of its facilities in addition to purchasing renewable energy through external providers.

Walmart has found that power purchase agreements (PPAs) are an effective approach to acquire renewable energy. Under a PPA, Walmart agrees to buy renewable power from an energy provider over time, but the provider owns, installs, and operates the renewable-energy systems. This market-based approach provides cost savings and greater price certainty. However, PPAs are not yet available in some countries and in many U.S. states. At the end of FY 2017, Walmart had over 480 renewable-energy projects in operation or under development in seven countries and 16 U.S. states.[32]

Solar energy features prominently in Walmart's renewable-energy portfolio. As of FY 2017, Walmart had 364 on-site solar installations throughout the United States, with a goal to have at least 480 solar installations in place by 2020.[33] Since 2007, Walmart has installed 620,000 solar photovoltaic panels at its facilities in the United States.[34] The company is also looking to include solar energy at its facilities outside of the United States. For example, Walmart India has expanded its use of rooftop solar technologies to power 90% of its buildings in India,[35] and Walmart's Massmart in South Africa is also beginning to pilot the use of renewable energy at some of its stores.

Walmart is making substantial progress on its renewable-energy goals, obtaining 26% (over 2.3 million kWh) of its electricity needs globally from renewable energy sources.[36] Since 2007, the company has added 600 MW of renewable-energy capacity worldwide. This is roughly equivalent to an emissions reduction of 40 million metric tons of CO_2e since 2005.[37]

As of 2016, Walmart ranked #9 among U.S.-based companies for the total amount of renewable energy procured, ranked #1 for on-site solar capacity in three out of the past four years, and ranked #1 for the number of sites with solar-photovoltaic systems.[38]

Walmart believes it can leverage its scale and purchasing power to help accelerate the adoption of renewable energy in the United States and abroad. Walmart is partnering with other major companies to increase global demand for renewable energy, accelerate innovation, and make renewable energy technologies more affordable.

Improving Energy Efficiency

Walmart's second core strategy to reduce energy intensity and emissions is to improve energy efficiency at its operations. Each year, Walmart makes thousands of incremental improvements to its store design, equipment, and technologies to improve its overall energy efficiency. For example, by the end of 2015, Walmart had upgraded 5,919 rooftop heating and cooling units at its stores in the United States. This saved the company US$ 5 million each year, while improving energy use by 50 million kWh and eliminating 35 million pounds of CO_2e.[39]

As of the end of FY 2017, Walmart had upgraded parking-lot lighting at 1,900 stores and 260 Sam's Club locations in the United States. This involved switching from high-intensity discharge lighting to more energy-efficient, light-emitting diode lighting technology, saving the company electricity and maintenance costs.[40]

Walmart has been successful in creating internal competitions to help reduce energy use. For example, in Argentina, Walmart launched a competition for its associates to identify energy-efficiency opportunities and to encourage the adoption of more responsible energy-use behaviors. The initiative resulted in a 5% decrease in energy consumption from March to December 2016 for its stores in Argentina.[41]

Finally, Walmart partners with its suppliers to help identify opportunities to improve energy efficiency. Walmart has trained more than 500 factory employees, particularly those in China, to use a web-based tool called the Resource Efficiency Deployment Engine (RedE) that helps factories identify opportunities to improve energy efficiency. The result: "From program launch through 2015, RedE has facilitated the completion of 118 individual factory efficiency projects, with reported factory cost savings of more than $2.8 million, energy savings of more than 45 million kWh, and GHG emission reductions of more than 33 thousand metric tons."[42]

Improving Facility Refrigeration Systems

The third core strategy that Walmart is implementing to reduce energy intensity and emissions is to upgrade its refrigeration, heating, and cooling systems. Refrigeration, heating, and cooling equipment accounts for as much as 30% to 50% of a building's energy consumption.[43] As a result, Walmart looks for improvement opportunities in the use of refrigeration and air-cooling equipment in its stores, distribution centers, and the company's delivery vehicles.

Walmart is focused on three areas to reduce energy use and improve refrigeration-system performance:

1. Use best practices for maintenance and monitoring.
2. Use common specifications for high-efficiency systems that provide a lower total cost of ownership.
3. Transition from hydrofluorocarbon-refrigerant gases to the use of lower-impact gases and refrigeration techniques.

Maximizing Trucking-Fleet Efficiency

Walmart's fourth core strategy to reduce energy intensity and emissions is to maximize the efficiency of its trucking fleet. With nearly 6,000 trucks logging millions of miles each year in the United States alone, Walmart is eager to find ways to deliver more products while driving fewer miles.

Using 2015 data as a baseline, Walmart proceeded to implement new initiatives, such as "effective driving techniques" (minimizing idle time and progressive shifting), "advanced tractor-trailer technologies" (electrification, light-weighting, advanced control systems, improved aerodynamics, and fuel-efficient tires), and "improved processes and systems to drive efficient loading and routing of merchandise." The results have been impressive: Walmart's fleet efficiency doubled in the United States since 2005, saving nearly US$ 1 billion and eliminating nearly 650,000 metric tons of greenhouse gases in 2015.[44]

To help drive innovation, Walmart will soon be rolling its fleet-efficiency goals into the broader goal of using 100% renewable energy. The company is also looking at innovations in automation, advanced aerodynamics, short-range communications, and safety technologies, such as sensors and detection equipment, electrification, and alternative fuel. Finally, Walmart is working with suppliers and regulators to build next-generation transportation networks that are safe, environmentally friendly, efficient, responsive, reliable, flexible, and cost-effective.

Reducing Waste

Walmart's second major goal related to pollution, climate change, and ocean acidification is to eliminate waste in its operations. To be more specific, Walmart aims to achieve zero waste in its operations in the United States, Canada, the United Kingdom, and Japan by 2025. The company has adopted the "zero-waste" definition put forth by the Zero Waste International Alliance, which calls for 90% or more diversion of all discarded resources from landfills, incinerators, and the environment. The company intends to divert waste in all markets as fast as infrastructure and best practices allow.

Walmart's strategies to accomplish its zero-waste goal include measuring waste in its operations, looking for opportunities to reduce waste, and improving water stewardship in its operations.

Measuring Waste

The prerequisite for any effort to eliminate waste is to develop a consistent methodology for measuring the amount of waste that is generated and disposed in landfills. To do this, Walmart conducted periodic studies in different markets to collect data on various categories of waste, such as cardboard, plastics, metals, food waste, glass, wood, tenant waste, and residual waste. The most recent study included facilities in Brazil, Canada, Central America, China, and Mexico.

Walmart also created a standardized waste-management data system that measures waste diversion, including energy and water data, at the country, region, and store levels. This system automates and streamlines data collection from hundreds of waste vendors and food banks around the world and helps Walmart identify opportunities to reduce waste. In 2016, a waste-management data system was launched in the United States and South America. Walmart is now in the process of launching the tool in Asia, Canada, the United Kingdom, and South Africa.

Eliminating Waste

To eliminate nonfood waste, Walmart looks for opportunities to reduce the amount of materials it uses, and donates or recycles goods that can't be sold. For example, to strike a balance between too much packaging (creating unnecessary waste) and too little packaging (resulting in damaged products), Walmart created a tool for buyers, replenishment teams, and sourcing teams to optimize the size of corrugated cardboard-shipping cartons for its apparel orders. This has helped Walmart reduce the overall number of boxes shipped by 8.1 million (compared with FY 2015) while saving nearly 6.3 million pounds of corrugate, preventing more than 7,800 MT of greenhouse gases and eliminating US$ 15.3 million in operational costs.[45] Walmart has also identified opportunities to save money and reduce waste by using lower-gauge plastic bags to protect apparel during shipping.

Walmart is moving towards the use of reusable packing containers in place of cardboard boxes and shrink wrap. By moving from cardboard to reusable packing containers, Walmart can lower its solid waste by 85% and reduce greenhouse-gas emissions by 31%. This will take some time and effort to implement since it involves changes to the company's operations and infrastructure, such as establishing regional centers to consolidate and wash the reusable containers. In the United Kingdom, Walmart's Asda stores have reused over 1.25 million trays, which has eliminated the need for cardboard packaging for those items.[46]

Another approach that Walmart is taking to cut down on waste involves refurbishing, donating, or recycling products. In the United States, Walmart has set up four refurbishing centers to fix returned and damaged phones, tablets, televisions, computers, and game consoles so that these products can be repaired and resold at a discount. More than six million electronic products were refurbished in FY 2017.[47] If a product can't be sold, then Walmart looks for the highest-value purpose for those items, which is typically a donation to charity. Walmart donated 13,000 tons of unsold durable goods in FY 2017.[48] For products that can't be refurbished or donated, Walmart creates an incentive for its stores to recycle these items by giving any income generated from recycling back to the store.

Walmart has similar processes in place to eliminate food waste. The company measures the amount of food waste that is generated and uses forecasting, ordering, and selling tools to increase product sell-through and prevent food waste. Food that is not purchased by consumers is donated to a variety of organizations that distribute it to people in need. Food that is no longer edible is converted into animal feed, compost, or energy.

Through these efforts, Walmart has been able to divert 82% of unsold products and packaging in the United States and 77% of unsold products and packaging globally.[49]

Improving Water Stewardship

Walmart's third waste-reduction strategy is focused on water stewardship. Compared with many other industries, the retail industry doesn't use much water directly. However, more than 20% of Walmart's operations are in areas that are projected to face high levels of water stress by 2025.[50] As a result, Walmart is pursuing the following initiatives to improve its water use efficiency, particularly in regions that face water scarcity:

- **Selection and monitoring of efficient water fixtures and technologies.** Walmart uses efficient fixtures and technologies in the design of its facilities, and it monitors usage to quickly identify and repair leaks.
- **Redesign of processes to reduce water use.** For example, Walmart has been able to change its trailer-washing processes to reduce the amount of water used to wash each of its thousands of tractor-trailers from 550 gallons per wash to as little as 195 gallons per wash. Walmart is now able to reclaim and reuse up to 86% of the water used for the trailer wash.[51]
- **Creation of on-site facilities to treat and reuse water.** For example, Walmart de Mexico has implemented 760 on-site water-treatment plants in Mexico.[52]
- **Harvesting of rainwater to reduce its water footprint.** As an example, Massmart in South Africa is harvesting rainwater in its Massbuild division and is capturing condensate water from many of Makro's refrigeration plants.
- **Construction and maintenance of wetlands.** Walmart has created nearly 150 wetlands on its properties in the United States. Some of these wetlands have been donated to organizations that preserve and maintain them. For example, in Logan, Utah, Walmart donated to the City of Logan a 3.21-acre wetland that was constructed to mitigate the impact to small streams while building a Supercenter. The wetland will be maintained by local volunteers and professionals to provide a habitat for local plants and wildlife.

Overharvesting

When it comes to the biodiversity threat of overharvesting, most companies tackle the issue by greening their supply chain, and Walmart is no exception. Many of the company's 100,000+ suppliers directly consume natural resources to create the products they deliver to Walmart. As you can imagine, it's not easy to ensure that 100,000 suppliers are adopting best practices in sustainability. How does Walmart attempt to tackle this challenge?

For starters, Walmart includes sustainability criteria in performance evaluations for its merchant managers who are responsible for making buying decisions worth billions of dollars. Granted, it's only one of a handful of performance targets, but it does play a role in modifying behavior.

Next, Walmart introduced a big data initiative to capture sustainability-related data from its suppliers. The company created its own supplier Sustainability Index and supplier scorecards based on key learnings from its participation in The Sustainability Consortium, a group composed of large retail and consumer-products companies. The Sustainability Index contains data from the entire product life cycle, including raw-material sourcing, manufacturing, distribution, retail sales, consumer use, and end-of-life product disposal. The Sustainability Index helps Walmart identify material environmental and social impacts and improvement opportunities across its product life cycle.

Walmart then created up to 15 key performance indicators in the form of survey questions that are sent to its 100,000+ suppliers and used to measure sustainability performance for each product category. The responses are collected using SAP's Product Stewardship Network and used to generate a variety of product-category heat maps, supplier scorecards, and impact-area dashboards. These decision-support tools are used to identify improvement opportunities, help suppliers continuously improve, identify new sustainability projects, and create a more sustainable product portfolio. To expand on this work, Walmart is now pilot-testing the use of blockchain technology to create a digitized industry standard for supply-chain traceability from farm to fork.

Walmart is also using data to provide greater product transparency to customers, so it's easy to understand what goes into products and how products are made. For example, Walmart now uses a "Great for You" icon for whole and processed foods that contain whole foods with below-threshold levels of fats, sodium, and added sugars.

Profitable-Conservation Summary

As you can see, Walmart is certainly involved in a wide variety of profitable-conservation efforts that are good for business, biodiversity, and wildlife. One of the challenges that Walmart will likely face in its role as a sustainability leader is to continue to advance its sustainability goals while adhering to the company's mission statement: "We save people money so they can live better."[53] Cost is a primary driver in Walmart's purchasing decisions, and low cost will often conflict with the price of sustainable products.

CEO Doug McMillon offers some insight on how Walmart intends to tackle this challenge: "When we get it right, customers are able to shop at ease, knowing we did the work for them. They know that the products on our shelves and website were produced at a low 'true cost' for all—not just in terms of being the best value, but in terms of whether they enhance the environment and the lives of all the people who helped produce them."[54]

Walmart is doing some great work regarding profitable conservation, and it will be interesting to see how far Walmart takes the "true-cost" concept in the coming years as it continues to take a leadership role in corporate sustainability.

Chapter 10 Endnotes

1. Walmart, "Walmart Locations Around the World—United States." Walmart Corporate: We Save People Money so They Can Live Better." Accessed June 17, 2018. https://corporate.walmart.com/our-story/locations/united-states#/united-states.
2. National Fish and Wildlife Foundation, "Acres for America." Accessed June 17, 2018. http://www.nfwf.org/acresforamerica/Pages/home.aspx.
3. Walmart, "2017 Global Responsibility Report," 81.
4. Ibid.
5. Ibid., 82.
6. National Fish and Wildlife Foundation, "Acres for America Program Announces $2.6 Million in Grants across Five States." December 13, 2016. Accessed June 17, 2018. http://www.nfwf.org/whoweare/mediacenter/pr/Pages/acres_16-1213.aspx.
7. Ibid.
8. Ibid.
9. Ibid.

10. Ibid.
11. Mike Hower, "APP, Cargill plant U.N. deforestation pledge for 2030." GreenBiz. September 26, 2014. Accessed June 17, 2018. https://www.greenbiz.com/blog/2014/09/26/app-cargill-un-deforestation-pledge.
12. Note 3, supra, 104.
13. Ibid., 106.
14. Ibid., 105.
15. Ibid., 106.
16. Walmart, "Green Roof Performance: A cost-benefit analysis based on Walmart's Chicago store." January 31, 2013, 6–8. Accessed June 17, 2018. http://cdn.corporate.walmart.com/95/ab/ecb63ba44f51bec6f9aa42c73a9e/walmart-2013-green-roof-report.pdf.
17. Ibid., 13.
18. Ibid.
19. Ibid.
20. Ibid., 20.
21. Ibid.
22. Ibid.
23. Ibid.
24. Ibid., 27.
25. Ibid., 29.
26. Ibid.
27. Ibid.
28. Ibid., 32.
29. Note 3, supra, 52.
30. Ibid., 54.
31. Ibid.
32. Ibid., 56.
33. Ibid., 57.
34. Ibid.
35. Ibid.
36. Ibid., 56.

37. Ibid.
38. Ibid.
39. Ibid., 60.
40. Ibid.
41. Ibid.
42. Walmart, "Reducing energy intensity and emissions." Walmart Corporate—We save People Money So They Can Live Better. Accessed June 17, 2018. https://corporate.walmart.com/2016grr/enhancing-sustainability/reducing-energy-intensity-and-emissions.
43. Ibid.
44. Ibid.
45. Note 42, supra.
46. Note 3, supra, 70–71.
47. Ibid., 72.
48. Ibid.
49. Ibid., 181.
50. Ibid., 77.
51. Ibid., 78.
52. Ibid.
53. Walmart, "Our History." Walmart Corporate—We save People Money so They Can Live Better. Accessed June 17, 2018. https://corporate.walmart.com/our-story/our-history.
54. Walmart, "A Message from our CEO." Walmart Corporate—We save People Money so They Can Live Better. Accessed June 17, 2018. https://corporate.walmart.com/2016grr/a-message-from-our-ceo.

CHAPTER 11

Profitable-Conservation Case Study: NEC Corporation (Japan)

"To remain an essential company in the eyes of society in 5 years, 10 years and beyond, NEC will create new value by always keeping abreast of what constitutes value for its customers and society."
—Takashi Niino, President and CEO, NEC

Company Overview

For our fourth and final profitable-conservation case study, we're off to Japan where we'll look at NEC Corporation, a multinational provider of information technology (IT) services and products. Headquartered in the Minato ward of Tokyo, NEC has over 107,000 employees worldwide who support four lines of business:

1. **Public business.** IT solutions, such as network, sensor, and analysis technologies for Japanese and foreign governments, governmental agencies, local governments, and other public institutions.
2. **Enterprise business.** IT solutions for private-sector companies in the manufacturing, retail and services, and finance industries. These solutions include the use of information-communication-and-tech-

nology assets, such as Internet of things (IoT) and artificial intelligence (AI), to support value-chain innovation.

3. **Telecom-carrier business.** Network-control platform systems and operating services to support telecom operations.
4. **System-platform business.** A variety of business products, such as terminals, network equipment, computers, software, and integrated-service platforms, which support IoT.

NEC is also a leader in corporate sustainability. Corporate Knights recognized NEC as one of the "Global 100 Most Sustainable Corporations in the World" in 2011, 2013, and 2017,[1] so the company knows a thing or two about sustainability. Another reason why I chose NEC as the fourth case study is due to its contributions to biodiversity conservation through its expertise in IT and network technologies. These technology-based approaches may help you come up with innovative ideas on how your company can support biodiversity and wildlife-conservation efforts that leverage the technical expertise of your business.

NEC's vision is "a world where our natural environment is preserved, enabling all people to pursue their full potential."[2] The approach to accomplishing this vision is outlined in NEC's CSR Reports, sustainability pages on its internet site, and through the company's Environmental Charter. NEC's CSR Report 2017 follows the core set of the Global Reporting Initiative's G4 Sustainability Reporting Guidelines. The company is also a proponent of various standards developed by the International Organization for Standardization (ISO). NEC has achieved ISO 26000 certification for social responsibility, ISO 22301 certification for business continuity management, and ISO 14000 certification for environmental management.

In its Environmental Charter, NEC provides the following action plan to accomplish its goal to respect, preserve, and be in harmony with the environment:

1. Produce energy and resource-saving products while giving careful thought to environmental and safety issues in development and planning.
2. Encourage the development of environmental technology on all levels (production, sales, distribution, and use and disposal of a product) and introduce materials, engineering, and recycling methods that will minimize adverse effects on the environment.

3. Respect and adhere to national and regional environmental regulations and strive to strengthen and enforce even stricter NEC environmental standards.
4. Contribute positively to society through an environmental-management program with a global perspective while educating and raising the environmental consciousness of all company members.
5. Provide a structured administrative organization for environmental management, with executives in charge of different areas, to delegate responsibilities and always be in the forefront of environmental matters.
6. Maintain and strengthen an independent environmental-management system and implement improvement measures based on internal environmental company audits.
7. Contribute to environmental protection by continuously making public announcements on the latest NEC developments in environmental technologies and management methods.

With that introduction to NEC, let's focus on the specific actions that NEC is taking to address four major threats to biodiversity and wildlife: habitat destruction; invasive species; pollution, climate change, and ocean acidification; and overharvesting.

Habitat Destruction

As an IT and electronics company, NEC addresses habitat destruction through a variety of policies and procedures, IT solutions, volunteer opportunities for employees, and by greening its supply chain. The following policy statement underscores how NEC feels it can best conserve biodiversity:

> "The NEC Group understands the important role that biodiversity plays in building a sustainable society and places the highest value on international charters and frameworks concerned with conserving biodiversity. We will do our very best to minimize the impact of our business operations and the daily lives of our employees on local ecosystems and habitats, actively encourage our employees to take part in biodiversity conservation activities

and develop and provide our customers with IT solutions that will help conserve biodiversity."[3]

To put these statements into action, NEC created the following three Essential Principles that are specific to biodiversity:

1. **"Essential Principle 1: Deepen people's understanding of biodiversity.** To conserve biodiversity, people need to understand the impact their work or daily lives has on local ecosystems and habitats. We therefore need to ensure that our employees and their families, as well as our suppliers, have a thorough understanding of biodiversity.
2. **"Essential Principle 2: Act in such a way as to conserve biodiversity.** By forming links with local communities, schools, and nonprofit organizations, we can broaden the scope of our environmental and social contribution activities to include a wider range of programs for conserving biodiversity. If we consider the impact our business activities and daily lives has on local ecosystems and habitats, we can more readily act to conserve biodiversity.
3. **"Essential Principle 3: Use our business operations to help conserve biodiversity.** We can use our IT and network technologies to provide solutions that help people understand, conserve, and increase biodiversity."

Finally, NEC translates these three Essential Principles into five Action Guidelines:

1. "Raise the awareness and deepen the understanding of NEC Group employees about biodiversity so that they can act proactively at work and at home to conserve biodiversity.
2. "Strengthen links with local communities, schools, and nonprofit organizations to enable a broader range of biodiversity conservation activities.
3. "Actively develop and provide customers with IT and network solutions and technologies that help conserve biodiversity.
4. "Clarify the relationship with biodiversity at every link in the supply chain and at every stage of a product's lifecycle (design and development, procurement of parts and materials, production, transportation, sale, use, and disposal) so that everyone involved understands how to act to conserve biodiversity.

5. "Actively publish and distribute information about the measures the NEC Group is taking to conserve biodiversity."

These five actions for preserving biodiversity can be grouped into two general strategies: contributions through IT and contributions by employees.

Contributions through IT

Under this strategy, NEC uses its IT and network technologies to create solutions that monitor biodiversity and "help us live in harmony with ecosystems."[4] Existing products and technologies are modified and tailored to address specific biodiversity and wildlife-conservation challenges. These solutions are cocreated along with customers from a "social-value-design" approach that considers value from the point of view of people and society. These technologies are available for purchase by any interested individuals or organizations, just like any other NEC product.

Here are some examples of NEC products that were created as part of its contributions-through-IT strategy:

- **Radar system for surveillance of illegal logging.** NEC created satellite-mounted synthetic aperture radar that can be used to help identify illegal logging activities. The radar system is installed on a satellite and uses remote sensing of reflected radio waves. This approach makes it possible to collect data for a large area regardless of the weather or time of day. Collected data are compared with previously collected data to identify forested areas that are declining. If illegal logging activities are detected, then appropriate authorities are notified to investigate further.
- **Estimate of forest value.** This solution estimates forest resources by calculating the estimated ground and tree heights based on aerial photos that are superimposed on geographic-information-system maps. This approach reduces the need for manual interpretation and makes it possible to quickly analyze large forest areas at a relatively low cost.
- **Optical-analysis technology to monitor forest health.** Optical-analysis technology looks at the spectrum of light reflected from vegetation and other objects and compares it with existing light-spectrum data to determine the type and condition of plants. The sur-

face-reflectance data can be captured in any weather conditions. Spectrum cameras can be installed on an airplane or other craft, which makes it easy to observe and quantify the ecology of remote forests that are difficult to access.

- **Headcount-estimation tool for animal counts.** NEC created a unique headcount-estimation tool that uses a convolutional neural network to estimate the number and density of animals in a given area, even under congested conditions.
- **Marine-environment monitoring system.** Customized software and underwater sensors are used to collect real-time data for a wide variety of marine-environment characteristics, such as marine water temperature, acidity, and visibility. Observation and surveillance data can be provided 24 hours a day and cover broad areas of marine habitat.
- **Insect Identification Support Service, using image-recognition technology.** With this tool, farm workers, gardeners, researchers, and educators can photograph an insect with a smartphone or other device and quickly learn if the insect species is harmful to crops. The photograph is compared with an image database to help identify the species. Farmers can use this information to select appropriate pest-control measures that are effective for that specific insect.
- **Prevention of bird strikes.** To help reduce the risk of airplane collisions with birds during takeoff and landing, NEC created a system that constantly monitors the presence of birds in and around airports.
- **Surveillance and control of wildlife.** This system detects wildlife through sensors that are placed at regular intervals along a fence, and it can send out a warning if a certain point is crossed. This can help prevent wildlife from harming crops or livestock. The sensors can also be combined with a surveillance camera to confirm and track wildlife.

Contributions by Employees

NEC's contributions-by-employees strategy for protecting biodiversity includes a variety of activities that increase employee awareness and understanding about the importance of biodiversity. Here are a few examples:

- **Conservation of an endangered species of damselfly.** At NEC's Abiko Plant in Japan, there is a spring-fed pond where an endangered damselfly—*Copera tokyoensis*—has been confirmed. In cooperation with Teganuma Aquatic Organism Research Association, NEC has established four dragonfly ponds and actively manages the ponds and surrounding vegetation to improve the natural environment for *Copera tokyoensis.* Four times a year, the company allows NEC employees and their families to participate in "living nature observations and invasive fish exterminations" to help protect the endangered damselfly; provide a habitat for a variety of plants, birds, and insects; and improve their understanding of biodiversity and conservation. These events also highlight the importance of removing invasive species of fish and plants from the ponds to support native plants and wildlife.[5]
- **NEC Paddy Making Project.** This project gives employees an opportunity to spend time in nature, participate in rice harvesting and sake-making activities, and help develop and verify new technologies that contribute to ecosystem observation and biodiversity conservation. Over the past seven years, the Paddy Making Project project has restored over 32,292 square feet of land in a ravine that had not been cultivated for over 30 years. The project began in 2004, in cooperation with NPO Asaza Fund, to improve the environmental awareness of NEC Group employees and their families in 2004, with a larger goal to help reestablish endangered Japanese crested ibises (*Nipponia nippon*) in the wild within the next 100 years. Extensive captive-breeding programs are in place in Japan and China to conserve the Japanese crested ibis. The Asaza project supports a long-term goal of the future coexistence of humans and wildlife in the Lake Kasumigaura watershed.[6]
- **Butterfly garden in Shiba Park.** At the headquarters building in Minato Ward of Tokyo, NEC holds lunch-time gardening events as well as family events on holidays to create a Biodiversity Garden that serves as a habitat for the chestnut-tiger (*Parantica sita*) butterflies during their migration. The Biodiversity Garden activities are planned and performed in cooperation with local governments, nonprofit organizations, and the local community. The gardening events give employees and families an opportunity to spend time in

nature while contributing to community development and biodiversity conservation.[7]

- **Student Birdathon.** NEC sponsors an annual Birdathon charity event in which students compete to find the most species of birds in a certain period and to raise the most money from supporters. The event helps raise awareness of birds and nature conservation through bird-watching activities, and the funds support bird-conservation efforts at the Ramsar Center Japan. The event has generated a total of US$ 204,313 in donations over the past 25 years.[8]
- **Lily conservation in Fuchu.** The only place in Japan where you can find a rare daylily called Musashino kisuge (*Hemerocallis middendorffii var. musashiensis*) growing in the wild is in the Tokyo Metropolitan Sengenyama Park in Fuchu. Since 2007, NEC employees and their families have partnered with the Sengenyama Nature Conservation Association to participate in activities to conserve the lily at Sengenyama Park by clearing underbrush and planting saplings. The activities also give participants an opportunity to learn about biodiversity in the park.[9]

Invasive Species

NEC does not have a formal program to address the threat of invasive species. However, as we saw earlier, NEC actively participates in the removal of invasive species at its Abiko facility, where the company hosts various employee activities that involve removing invasive fish and plants from on-site ponds that provide habitat for an endangered species of damselfly. These events are also used as an educational opportunity to teach how invasive species can negatively impact the environment for native species of plants and wildlife.

Pollution, Climate Change, and Ocean Acidification

For the biodiversity threats of pollution, climate change, and ocean acidification, NEC focuses its attention on activities in the areas of pollution prevention, environmental accounting, Design for the Environment (DfE), and climate-change mitigation.

Pollution Prevention

NEC has a robust pollution-prevention program that encompasses all areas of the value chain. The company uses a material-balance approach that looks at the mass of material entering and leaving the value chain and analyzes these mass-balance values to create improvement opportunities and performance measures that will reduce the company's impact on the environment. The various pollution-prevention initiatives and targets are summarized below:

- **Purchasing and procurement.** NEC has implemented a variety of green procurement policies and guidelines. Success measures are focused on compliance with the European Union's Restriction of Hazardous Substances (RoHS) Directive and Registration, Evaluation, Authorization, and Restriction of Chemicals (REACH) regulations. RoHS prohibits the use of various substances in the manufacture of electronic and electrical equipment, such as lead, mercury, and cadmium.
- **Research and development.** NEC actively looks for opportunities to use bioplastics in its products. "Bioplastics" are a type of biodegradable plastic that is made from biological substances rather than petroleum.
- **Manufacturing and sales**
  - **Reduce energy use.** NEC has set a goal to reduce the energy intensity of logistics (year-on-year) by 1% and has set an annual target to reduce electric-power usage in proportion to sales by 7.8% compared with FY 2013 levels.[10] To accomplish these targets, NEC has pursued the following initiatives:
    - Using fluorescent light bulbs only in every other light fixture.
    - Automatically switching off lights in offices at the headquarters building at a set time.
    - Adjusting air-conditioning temperatures.
    - Shutting down shared equipment (e.g., printers and individual air conditioners).
    - Inspecting heat-recovery equipment, such as thermostatic baths and ovens, heaters, and driers.

  - Installing energy-saving equipment (e.g., high-efficiency lighting, such as light-emitting diode (LED)).
  - Using building-wide, public-address systems to call for power-saving actions.
  - Following the Cool Biz initiative that allows employees to wear casual clothes (no jacket, open collar) in the office, including conference rooms. The office air-conditioning temperature for cooling is set at 28 degrees C. This policy applies from May 1 to October 31.
  - Using smart technologies (e.g., after implementing energy-efficiency improvements as part of the NEC Tamagawa Plant Smart Project in FY 2016, the facility was able to cut power consumption by 50% during the fiscal year).[11]

- **Reduce greenhouse gas and other air emissions.** NEC has set targets to reduce CO_2 emissions and maintain or reduce nitrogen oxide (NOx) and sulfur oxide (SOx) emissions to FY 2003 levels. In FY 2017, NEC was able to reduce CO_2 emissions by 10% compared with FY 2016, reduce total SOx emissions by 98% compared to FY 2003, and reduce NOx emissions by 96% compared to FY 2003.[12]
- **Reduce waste and properly process waste materials.** NEC targets related to reducing waste include maintaining or reducing paper purchases to FY 2006 levels, maintaining or reducing consumption of paper- and plastic-packaging materials to FY 2006 levels, and maintaining a 90% resource-reutilization rate for used products that have been recovered. In FY 2017, NEC decreased the amount of general waste and industrial waste generated by 27% compared with FY 2016. This accomplishment was achieved primarily through a reduction in the amount of waste generated from construction work. NEC's municipal-waste recycling rate is 97.5% while its industrial-waste recycling rate is 83.7%. The company also provides training on sorting trash to new employees and displays posters at trash-collection stations that make it easy to determine which bins should be used for diverse types of trash.[13]

- **Reduce the use of chemical substances.** NEC reviews the environmental impact and safety of chemicals in all phases of handling, including receipt, use, and disposal. The company looks for process improvements and production innovations that will help it reduce the consumption of chemical substances and replace harmful substances with safer ones.
- **Reduce water consumption and water pollution.** To reduce water consumption and pollution, NEC has set targets to maintain or reduce water consumption, biochemical oxygen demand, and chemical oxygen demand to FY 2003 levels. NEC uses voluntary water-quality standards that are more stringent than legally required standards and has pursued a variety of means to reduce water consumption. The company is also engaged in efforts to protect forests in catchment areas.[14]

- **Product use.** NEC looks for opportunities to reduce the amount of CO_2 emissions that are generated from consumer use of its products.
- **Disposal and recycling.** Since 1969, NEC has been promoting the collection and recycling of used information and telecommunication equipment. In 2005, the company established its NEC Refresh (refurbished) personal computer (PC) business. NEC also pursues a variety of initiatives to collect and recycle used ink cartridges, laser / LED cartridges, rechargeable batteries, and other products. NEC's recovery rate for used information equipment increased by 6% in 2017 compared with FY 2016. In FY 2016, the recycling rate (ratio of the weight of reused, material-recycled, and thermal-recycled items to the total weight of the collected IT devices) was nearly 99%. NEC's resource-reuse rate (ratio of the weight of materials that can be used as recycled products or resources to the total weight of the collected IT devices) was 93% in FY 2017.[15]

Environmental Accounting

Since 1998, NEC has been using environmental-accounting methods to evaluate the costs and benefits of the company's various environmental activities. For its environmental-cost calculations, NEC includes facility depreciation, rental / lease expenses, personnel, operational expenses, such as energy and maintenance costs, and other expenditures, such as payments to third parties. Environmental-benefit calculations include cost savings from reducing energy, resources, and waste, and improving processes while maintaining quality. The company does not include intangible or qualitative benefits in its environmental-accounting calculations. Quality is confirmed through NEC's environmental-audit program.

NEC applies its environmental-accounting methodology to the following areas:

- Prevention of global warming
- Effective resource utilization, such as the amount of chemicals and paper purchased
- Resource-recycling activities
- Material-handling compliance and risks, including the acquisition of legal licenses and training for emergency measures
- Design of environmentally friendly products
- Recovery of used products
- Personnel cost associated with environmental activities
- ISO-certification maintenance and environmental audits
- Environmental-education programs and job-specific training for employees who are in positions that have the potential to cause serious impacts to the environment
- Environment-related research and development
- Social activities and contributions to society
- Information disclosure, such as the creation and distribution of environmental reports, internet pages, newsletters, and responses to questions from outside of the company

This quantitative environmental-accounting approach has increased awareness of the economic impact of various environmental initiatives and has helped the company identify new improvement opportunities.

Design for the Environment

Since 1994, NEC has set company-wide product-assessment guidelines and systems to evaluate environmental design of its products, which includes the use of life-cycle assessment techniques. The key drivers for product development at NEC include quality, cost, delivery, ecology, global-warming prevention, resource recycling, environmental consciousness, and compliance.

By adopting a DfE program, NEC has been able to develop a variety of products that have a significantly smaller impact to the environment. For example, NEC has developed and commercialized a new bioplastic under the brand name NeCycle™ that uses plant resources as its primary raw material. Bioplastics are now being used in a variety of NEC products, such as PCs, projectors, mobile phones, lighting equipment, point-of-sale terminals, and mobile business terminals.

NEC has also adopted its own Eco Symbol label to identify products and services that meet NEC's environmental standards and are considered environmentally superior to conventional green products. In addition, an Eco Symbol Star label is placed on product packaging, catalogs, and websites for NEC products that meet NEC environmental standards for the Eco Symbol and are considered industry "top-runner" products.

Climate-Change Mitigation

NEC is taking proactive steps to address climate change, and it has created a variety of targets that are aimed at reducing CO_2 emissions as well as mitigating and adapting to climate change. Here are the climate-change targets towards which NEC is currently working:

- **Reducing emissions from business activities**[16]
    - 18% improvement in FY 2021 compared with FY 2013
    - 30% improvement in FY 2031 compared with FY 2013
    - 10-fold increase in the amount of renewable energy used in FY 2021 compared with FY 2012
    - Overall goal to achieve a level of CO_2 reduction that is five times the total volume of CO_2 emissions from its entire supply chain in FY 2021
- **Mitigating climate change**[17]
    - 23 million-ton reduction in emissions from customers and society through IT solutions in FY 2021
    - 50 million-ton reduction in emissions from customers and society through IT solutions in FY 2031

  - 30% improvement in product-energy efficiency in FY 2021 compared with products in FY 2014
  - 80% improvement in product-energy efficiency in FY 2031 compared with products in FY 2014
- **Adapting to climate change**
  - Provide solutions that help resolve social issues and prepare for the impacts of climate change

In July 2017, NEC created long-term, climate-change mitigation guidelines that it will use to guide its actions through 2050 to help the company achieve its climate-change targets. The climate-change mitigation guidelines include the following four core components:

1. **Zero CO_2 emissions from supply chains.** NEC's long-term goal is to reduce CO_2 emissions from business operations to "effectively zero."[18] To do this, NEC will use a combination of three strategies:
   - **Energy-saving technologies** that will reduce energy consumption. For example, NEC's data centers will use advanced technologies, such as phase-change cooling, waste-heat utilization, Internet of things, big data, AI, and the development and application of other innovations to reduce energy consumption.
   - **Renewable energy sources** will be used at NEC business sites and company-owned buildings and linked with large-capacity, electric-energy storage systems.
   - **Carbon offsets** that will take a variety of forms, such as offsetting CO_2 emissions generated from employee travel and offsetting CO_2 emissions that are generated from internet services. For example, when NEC operated an internet service provider called BIGLOBE (which it sold to KDDI Corporation in 2017), NEC created a program to plant trees to offset the CO_2 emissions caused by internet searches. BIGLOBE calculated that a single eucalyptus tree will absorb 400 kilograms of CO_2 over 20 years, which was equivalent to the CO_2 emitted by one million internet searches. As a result, NEC planted one eucalyptus tree in the NEC Forest located on Kangaroo Island, Australia, for each one million internet searches.

2. **Strict measures against climate-change risks in supply chains.** NEC will continue to improve its overall energy efficiency and collaborate with suppliers to reduce emissions. The company also plans to evaluate the impact of climate-change risks, such as water shortages, floods, landslides, and other disaster-related risks on the global supply chain, and work with its suppliers to mitigate these risks.
3. **Low-carbon society as the global target.** NEC plans to work with customers to cocreate solutions that will move society towards low CO_2 emissions through a variety of efforts designed to increase production and logistics efficiency, improve capacity-utilization rates, reduce food waste, and increase the use of renewable-energy sources through the deployment of large-scale, power-storage systems.
4. **Safe and secure society that is strong against climate-change risks.** NEC will partner with customers to cocreate solutions that will enable society to mitigate a variety of climate-change risks, such as the supply of energy, water, and food, as well as the prevention of health hazards.

Overharvesting

For the biodiversity threat of overharvesting, NEC focuses its efforts on reducing the environmental impacts across its entire supply chain. To do this, NEC has created a variety of Green Procurement policies and guidelines that are supported by supplier-training programs and validated through supply-chain audits. NEC also provides Green Procurement training to appropriate internal positions and roles and provides training to chemical-substance evaluators who evaluate and improve how suppliers manage their chemicals.

Since 2003, NEC has operated a green-certification system that covers procurement of hardware, software, and services. The goal of the green-certification system is to procure low-impact materials from environmentally conscious suppliers who use low-impact manufacturing processes. As part of NEC's Green Procurement guidelines, certain chemicals are banned for use in products or processes. Suppliers are required to create an environmental-management system, and NEC also requests that suppliers pursue a variety of environmental-conservation activities, which includes efforts to conserve biodiversity.

To assess supplier-environmental performance, NEC performs chemical-substance-content surveys for all purchased items and monitors CO_2 emissions data (validated by third-party vendors) related to the items it purchases from major suppliers. NEC pulls together this environmental-performance data into an internal database, along with cost, quality, and delivery-date data, and performs analyses to rate suppliers and assess products. Priority is given to green-certification suppliers who practice environmentally sound activities and to parts and materials that exhibit excellent characteristics from an environmental perspective.

Finally, NEC performs a variety of compliance-check measurements and supplier audits to ensure that suppliers are adhering to NEC policies and guidelines. For example, for high-risk parts, NEC obtains analysis data from suppliers, and then uses fluorescent X-ray analysis systems that are installed in NEC manufacturing plants to analyze and measure these parts. This approach helps NEC stay in compliance with the RoHS directive, which restricts the use of certain hazardous substances in electrical and electronic equipment.

Through these efforts, the company has maintained a green-procurement rate of 100% for its product-related materials.[19]

Profitable-Conservation Summary

As we've seen, NEC is engaged in a variety of environmental best practices and biodiversity-conservation efforts that utilize the company's strength in IT. While the company doesn't provide much data to help us assess the return on investment for specific biodiversity-conservation efforts, NEC does provide the following high-level, environmental-accounting summary of the cost and "economic effect" of different environmental programs for FY 2017.

Program	Investment	Cost	Economic Effect
Business-related costs (e.g., prevention of global warming, effective utilization of resources, resource recycling, risk minimization)	US$ 700,476	$6,603,156	$747,174

Program	Investment	Cost	Economic Effect
Upstream and downstream costs (e.g., design of environmentally friendly products, collection, recycling, and reuse of used products)	US$ 13,993	$475,762	$0
Management-activity costs (e.g., personnel expenses related to environmental activities, human-resource development, and environmental training of employees, ISO maintenance)	$17,724	$1,604,530	$0
Research-and-development costs	$0	$0	$0
Social-contribution activity costs (e.g., environmental-improvement measures and societal contributions)	$0	US$ 18,657	$0
Environmental-damages cost	$0	$0	$0
Total	$732,193	$8,702,105	$747,174

This table provides a good illustration of the challenge that all companies face when it comes to making conservation profitable. When a company adopts a cost-benefit methodology that does not consider intangible benefits, many environmental initiatives look like a losing proposition. However, NEC clearly must believe that there is value in pursing these environmental investments, whether they are in the form of employee satisfaction, consumer goodwill, or the anticipation of future trends.

All progressive companies hope that their efforts to be good stewards of the environment will give them an advantage over their competitors and lead to an increase in sales and revenue. This is where each of us, as consumers, has a vital role to play, as we'll explore in the next chapter.

Chapter 11 Endnotes

1. NEC, "CSR Report 2017," 23.
2. NEC, "NEC Environmental Charter." Accessed June 17, 2018. https://www.nec.com/en/global/eco/announce/charter/index.html.

3. NEC, "Principles for Conserving Biodiversity: Preserving Biodiversity." Accessed June 17, 2018. https://www.nec.com/en/global/eco/life/guide/index.html.

4. NEC, "Contributions through IT: Preserving Biodiversity." Accessed June 17, 2018. https://www.nec.com/en/global/eco/life/it/index.html.

5. NEC, "NEC Living Nature Observation Team in Abiko: Environment and Biodiversity." Accessed June 17, 2018. https://www.nec.com/en/global/community/environment/tombo.html.

6. Azasa Fund (Non-Profit Organization), "What Is Asaza Project?" Accessed June 17, 2018. http://www.asaza.jp/en/outline/about/.

7. NEC, "NEC Nature Quest in Shiba Park: Environment and Biodiversity." Accessed June 17, 2018. https://www.nec.com/en/global/community/environment/nature_quest.html.

8. NEC, "NEC Student Birdathon: Environment and Biodiversity." Accessed June 17, 2018. https://www.nec.com/en/global/community/environment/birdathon.html.

9. NEC, "NEC Green Conservation Activity in Fuchu: Environment and Biodiversity." Accessed June 17, 2018. https://www.nec.com/en/global/community/environment/green_preservation.html.

10. NEC, "Energy-saving Promotion System and Measures: Greenhouse Gases." Accessed June 17, 2018. https://www.nec.com/en/global/eco/issue/warming/nec_ec/index.html.

11. Ibid.

12. NEC, "CO_2 Emissions: Greenhouse Gases." Accessed June 17, 2018. https://www.nec.com/en/global/eco/issue/warming/gas/index.html; *see also* "Air, Soil, Water Quality: Reducing Environmental Impact." Accessed June 17, 2018. https://www.nec.com/en/global/eco/issue/chemical/a_s_w.html.

13. NEC, "Waste Products: Reducing Environmental Impact." Accessed June 17, 2018. https://www.nec.com/en/global/eco/issue/waste/index.html.

14. NEC, "Water: Reducing Environmental Impact." Accessed June 18, 2018. https://www.nec.com/en/global/eco/issue/chemical/warter.html.

15. NEC, "Collection and Recycling Activities: Collection and Recycling." Accessed June 18, 2018. https://www.nec.com/en/global/eco/recycle/result/index.html.

16. NEC, "NEC Group Environmental Management Action Plan 2020/2030: Climate Change Mitigation Measures." Accessed June 18, 2018. https://www.nec.com/en/global/eco/announce/environmental-plan/index.html.

17. Ibid.

18. NEC, "Course of Action for Climate Change Towards 2050: Climate Change Mitigation Measures." Accessed June 18, 2018. https://www.nec.com/en/global/eco/announce/policy_guideline/index.html.

19. NEC, "Green Procurement Guidelines: Environmentally Friendly Products | NEC." Accessed June 18, 2018. https://www.nec.com/en/global/eco/product/green/index.html#greenprocurementguidelines.

CHAPTER 12

Conclusion

"The Earth is what we all have in common."
—Wendell Berry

Call to Action

Hopefully, this book has clarified the role that businesses can play in biodiversity and wildlife conservation. If you want to read more, please visit my website at www.profitableconservation.com where you will find additional case studies, success stories, and best practices of companies representing a variety of industries from all over the world. Also feel free to send me your own success stories and best practices, and I will be happy to share them with others. I can be reached at mark@profitableconservation.com.

The goal of this book is to highlight the important role that businesses can and do play in protecting biodiversity and wildlife. However, keep in mind that this is just one piece of the conservation puzzle. There are many other effective approaches to protecting biodiversity and wildlife, such as legal action, government policy, scientific research, and grassroots activism. Each of these approaches has a key role to play, and there are many great organizations that are leading the charge in these areas at the local, national, and international levels.

The end of any presentation or book should include a call to action. Before I sign off, here's a call to action that applies to each one of us, as individuals, regardless of what we do for a living. Whether we work for a large corporation or a small business, or whether we run our own business in the comfort of our pajamas at home, here are three ideas to consider on how you can help conserve biodiversity and wildlife every day.

Change the World, One Purchase at a Time

One of the most significant things that you can do to make the world a better place, as defined by each of us, is to make purchasing decisions that reflect your values. Speak through your purchases. Companies will listen. It's back to the Economics 101 lesson about supply and demand. Companies provide products and services that are in demand. If you continue to demand cheap products and services that are not good from an environmental, health, or social perspective, that's what companies will continue to produce and supply. If instead you purchase products and services that are aligned with your values and ideals, companies will supply those products and services.

Companies respond to consumer preferences based on your actual purchases, not your stated intentions. Your stated intentions are not irrelevant, but they pale in comparison to actual sales data. As the tired saying goes, "Actions speak louder than words."

In some cases, there may be a significant cost difference between a product that is produced in alignment with your beliefs and one that isn't. It simply may not be a viable option given the reality of how much money you have in your wallet. In other cases, the cost difference may be small and well within your budget. For some products, you may find that there is no cost difference at all.

Never underestimate the power of your purchasing decisions. They can cause a ripple effect that leads to meaningful change. The choice to create a cleaner, healthier world that helps protect biodiversity and wildlife is up to each one of us, every day. Make purchases that reflect your values.

Dunna Chuck Bruck!

One of my biggest pet peeves—one that even trumps rubbernecking—is littering. When I see someone throw trash or a cigarette out of a car window, I feel a sudden urge to jump out of the car to pick up the cigarette or trash from the ground and throw it back in that person's vehicle. Of course, I don't act on that urge, but it's fun to think about. Instead, I usually just harbor negative, judgmental feelings about that person. What can I say? I'm a work in progress.

Short of throwing cigarettes and trash back at the people who litter, you can make it clear to those around you that littering is not cool. Lead by example. Listen to the wisdom of that bastion of coolness Woodsy Owl: "Give a hoot—don't pollute!" Okay, Woodsy Owl may not instill much fear or motivation, so perhaps you can think of "Don't Mess with Texas" or a road sign I saw in the Shetland Islands, "Dunna Chuck Bruck!" Most people don't know what the heck that means, but the thought of William Wallace (of *Braveheart* fame) yelling that while chasing after us with a medieval weapon would probably get our attention.

Make Your Land Permeable to Wildlife

About now, you're probably expecting to see the "reduce, reuse, recycle" thing, but that's low-hanging fruit that everyone knows about already. Let's look at another, not-so-common thing that you can do. Ensure that your business and home are friendly to wildlife. No, it doesn't mean that we want to have bears wandering around our kitchen—although that did happen to one of our neighbors when my family lived in Colorado! What it does mean is that you can maintain native vegetation and use natural cleaning and landscaping products in your household, which support a healthy and diverse community of insects, birds, and other critters.

As more and more green space gets gobbled up in our cities, the concept of wildlife corridors or linkages becomes more important. Roughly 7% of the global ocean and 15% of global land are designated as protected today.[1] While that might sound like a good chunk of land, in scientific circles, this patchwork of fragmented land is woefully inadequate in terms of providing sufficient habitat for wide-ranging species and for conserving global biodiversity. Look for opportunities to make your land more permeable to wildlife so that animals can move between regions that are separated by roads or development. This gives animals access to resources they need to survive and facilitates the exchange of individuals between populations, which helps prevent inbreeding and improve genetic diversity. Plus, it's just plain fun to have wildlife visiting our backyard!

There are plenty of scientific debates about the pros and cons of establishing a wildlife corridor; however, in terms of what you can do as an individual, it's quite simple. You can keep part of your commercial and residential property in a natural state, using native plants that support insect pollinators, birds, and other animals. Efforts by landowners to voluntarily preserve natural vegetation and healthy, functioning ecosystems can affect far more land than formal, incentive-based agreements that are facilitated through land-stewardship programs. You may have to do a little homework to identify best practices that make sense for where you live and work, but there are plenty of free, helpful resources to guide you. Think of ways that you can make your land, at home or at work, as permeable as possible to native wildlife.

The list of ecosystem services that you can support is long. Your actions can help with air and water purification, flood and drought mitigation, waste detoxification and decomposition, soil generation and renewal, crop and natural-vegetation pollination, seed and nutrient dispersal, biodiversity maintenance, moderation of temperature extremes and urban heat islands, and mitigation of the impact of wind and waves. When all else fails, you can always do things with your land that contribute to the aesthetic beauty of your community and help lift the spirit of people who pass by your little corner of the world.

If you own many acres of land, you can use it to link habitats for large animals, such as deer, mountain lions, and bear. If you have nothing but a small ledge in an urban landscape, a potted plant or birdfeeder can still make a difference for birds or insects. You can also look at options to install a rooftop garden or living wall that serves to reduce energy consumption, decrease the rate and volume of rain runoff, lessen the urban heat-island effect, and provide green space for humans, birds, and insects to enjoy. These can be win-win situations that save money, look attractive, and are good for wildlife and the health of the environment. Regardless of your situation, there's always something that you can do to contribute to a cleaner, healthier environment that supports wildlife and biodiversity.

Parting Words

Humans have the power to destroy or protect nature, so let's use that power wisely. Some of us may get involved politically, others will address it through environmental regulations, and still others will find their niche in grassroots activism. Many of us will feel called to financially support organizations that buy and protect critical land for wildlife to help us reach the *Half-Earth* goal. Regardless of your approach or beliefs, it's easy to do your part to help protect biodiversity and wildlife. Make purchasing decisions that are aligned with your values. Make your land attractive and permeable to native wildlife. At the very least, Dunna Chuck Bruck!

In more eloquent terms, let's end with a quote from three individuals who developed an environmental ethic from very different backgrounds and experiences:

"Here is your country. Cherish these natural wonders, cherish the natural resources, cherish the history and romance as a sacred heritage, for your children and your children's children. Do not let selfish men or greedy interests skin your country of its beauty, its riches or its romance."
—Theodore Roosevelt

"Humankind has not woven the web of life. We are but one thread within it. Whatever we do to the web, we do to ourselves. All things are bound together … all things connect."
—Chief Seattle

"You cannot get through a single day without having an impact on the world around you. What you do makes a difference, and you have to decide what kind of difference you want to make."
—Jane Goodall

Chapter 12 Endnote

1. Protected Planet, "The lag effect in the World Database on Protected Areas." June 18, 2018. https://protectedplanet.net/c/the-lag-effect-in-the-world-database-on-protected-areas.

Glossary

aerial plankton: Tiny life forms that float and drift in the air, carried by the current of the wind.

algal blooms: A rapid increase in the population of algae in an aquatic system, which can harm aquatic life by releasing biotoxins or lowering the amount of oxygen in natural waters. It may occur from an excess of nutrients (e.g., phosphorus and nitrogen) from human-related activities such as runoff from agriculture and development and pollution from septic systems and sewers.

area protected: An area protected from any harm during operational activities and where the environment remains in its original state with a healthy and functioning ecosystem.

area restored: An area used during or affected by operational activities where remediation measures have either restored the environment to its original state or to a state where it has a healthy and functioning ecosystem.

avoidance: A strategy involving leaving areas of land alone, free from development or business operations. In practice, an avoidance strategy may also involve monitoring and maintaining the integrity of the habitat.

avoidance zones: Areas of land that will be left alone, free from development or business operations.

biodiversity (see **biological diversity**)

biological diversity: The variety of life on Earth, which can be described at the gene, species, population, and ecosystem levels. While each of these levels is important to consider, the most common unit of measurement for biological diversity is the species.

biodiversity hotspot: To qualify as a biodiversity hotpot, a region must meet two strict criteria: (1) a minimum of 1,500 endemic vascular plants; and (2) and 30% or less of its original natural vegetation. There are 35 of these irreplaceable and threatened regions around the world.

biodiversity offsets: Measurable conservation outcomes resulting from actions designed to compensate for significant residual, adverse, biodiversity impacts arising from development plans or projects after appropriate prevention and mitigation measures have been taken.

biological control (of invasive species): The use of insect predators or plant diseases to kill invasive species.

biological invasion: A process where individuals of a species that aren't native to a region arrive with human assistance and spread in their new home.

bioplastics: A type of biodegradable plastic made from biological substances rather than petroleum.

capitals: In the context of integrated reporting, capitals refer to resources and relationships that are used to create value over time. This may include financial, manufactured, intellectual, human, social and relationship, and natural capital.

carbon offset: Also known as **greenhouse-gas offset**, a credit for greenhouse-gas reductions achieved by one party that can be purchased and used to compensate (offset) the emissions of another party.

catchments: Areas where water is collected by the natural landscape and flows into a creek, a river, a dam, a lake, an ocean, or a groundwater system.

chemical control (of invasive species): The use of herbicides to kill plants and prevent their return.

chytridiomycosis: An emerging infectious disease of amphibians caused by an aquatic fungal pathogen, *Batrachochytrium dendrobatidis*.

closed-loop system: A system in which every component is recirculated within that same system for as long as possible, with the goal of reusing, recycling, or biodegrading all materials involved to produce zero waste.

corridor: Any space that facilitates the movement of plants and animals among core habitat fragments. The goal of a corridor is to maintain or improve the number of distinct species and the health of species in an area.

currencies (for biodiversity offsets): Metrics that enable us to make comparisons between the gains and losses of the impacted and offset land, providing a common unit for trade or exchange.

Design for the Environment: Design approach to reduce the overall environmental impact of a product, process, or service, which considers environmental impacts across its life cycle.

ecosystem services: The benefits people derive from ecosystems. This includes provisioning services or goods (e.g., food, wood, and other raw materials) as services such as pollination of crops, prevention of soil erosion and water purification, and a vast array of cultural services like recreation and a sense of place.

edge effects: Changes in habitat characteristics along the habitat's boundary or "edge."

endemic species: Native species that are found only within a particular region.

energy assessment (see **energy audit**)

energy audit: Also known as energy assessment, an evaluation of a building's energy systems to identify opportunities to reduce energy use.

eutrophication: Enrichment of an ecosystem with chemical nutrients, typically compounds containing nitrogen, phosphorus, or both. Can be a natural process or occur from human-related activities such as runoff from agriculture and development and pollution from septic systems and sewers.

extended producer responsibility: Also known as **producer takeback** or **product takeback**, a product and waste-management system in which manufacturers (instead of the consumer or government) take responsibility for the environmentally safe management of their product when it is no longer useful or discarded. This approach may be voluntary or regulatory-driven.

gall: Abnormal growths that occur on leaves, twigs, roots, or flowers of many plants, caused by irritation and/or stimulation of plant cells due to feeding or egg-laying by insects such as aphids, midges, wasps, or mites.

gray infrastructure: Man-made solutions that typically involve concrete and steel.

green building: Planning, design, construction, and operation of buildings in a way that minimizes the overall impact on the environment.

green computing: Also known as **green IT**, the manufacture, use, and disposal of personal computers, servers, and other IT hardware in environmentally friendly ways.

greenhouse gases: Gases that trap heat in the atmosphere, such as carbon dioxide, methane, nitrous oxide, and fluorinated gases.

greenhouse-gas offset (see **carbon offset**)

green infrastructure: Natural systems that are managed to address urban challenges, such as stormwater management, climate adaptation, clean water, and healthy soils.

green IT (see **green computing**)

green roof: Also known as **living roof**, a roof of a building that is partially or completely covered with vegetation.

green walls (see **living walls**)

greening the supply chain: Actions that are designed to improve the environmental performance of an organization's supply chain.

habitat destruction: The complete destruction of a habitat or, more commonly, habitat fragmentation, where a large, continuous area of a habitat is divided into two or more fragments.

habitat fragmentation: A large, continuous area of a habitat divided into two or more fragments.

heat-island effect: Elevated temperatures in urban areas compared to rural, less-developed areas.

hybrid infrastructure: Utilizes a combination of green and gray infrastructure to provide a solution to a challenge.

indigenous species: Native species that are found within the region specified and in other regions.

integrated report: One report that pulls together analyses of financial and non-financial performance rather than having separate financial and corporate social responsibility reports.

integrated water-resource management: Processes that promote the coordinated development and management of water, land, and other resources in a way that creates benefits to the economy and society without harming vital ecosystems.

introduced species: A species that arrives in an area with human help, which includes species that don't establish populations or spread from the point of arrival, and doesn't become invasive unless the population spreads from the point of arrival.

invasive species: "Invasive" refers to the behavior of spreading in the new region from the point of arrival; an "invasive species" is a species that spreads in the new region from the point of arrival.

IUCN Red List of Threatened Species: Established in 1964, this list has become the world's most comprehensive information source on the global conservation status of animal, fungi, and plant species.

Leadership in Energy and Environmental Design: A globally recognized framework and rating system used to create efficient, healthy, and cost-saving green buildings.

life-cycle assessment: A technique for assessing the potential environmental impacts of a product, process, or activity throughout its life cycle, from the extraction of raw materials to processing, transport, use, and disposal.

linkage: Any space that facilitates the movement of plants and animals between core habitat fragments.

linkage project: A project that is designed to make your property more permeable to wildlife.

living roof (see **green roof**)

living walls: Also known as **green walls**, vertical gardens that can be found indoors or outdoors.

mechanical control (of invasive species): Physically removing plants from the environment, which can be done through cutting, mowing, pulling, or suffocating plants by covering them with plastic sheeting.

native species: "Native" refers to the place of origin; "native species," which comes in two forms—endemic or indigenous—refers to a species that is living within its natural range.

natural capital: All renewable and nonrenewable environmental resources and processes that provide goods or services to support the past, current, or future prosperity of an organization.

overharvesting: A broad term that refers to the harvesting of a renewable resource at an unsustainable rate. The term can apply to plants, fish stocks, forests, grazing pastures, and game animals.

permeability: In a "permeable landscape," wildlife can move relatively freely from one area to another.

pest: A destructive insect or other animal that attacks crops, food, or livestock.

pollution: The introduction of contaminants (e.g., chemicals, light, noise, or heat) into the natural environment where they may cause negative changes.

producer takeback (see **extended producer responsibility**)

product takeback (see **extended producer responsibility**)

profitable conservation: Actions that benefit business, biodiversity, and wildlife.

protected area: Locations that are protected and managed, through legal or other effective means, to achieve the long-term conservation of natural, ecological, or cultural values.

reduce, reuse, and recycle: Reduce the amount of trash we create, reuse trash so that we don't have to throw it out, and recycle trash to make new goods that can be sold again.

rehabilitation: The process of repairing ecosystem processes, but not to the pre-existing, historical trajectory of the ecosystem.

remediation: The process of reducing or stopping pollution that threatens the health of people or wildlife.

restoration: The process of recovering an ecosystem that has been damaged or destroyed and returning the ecosystem to its historical trajectory.

SLOSS debate: Short for "single large or several small" habitats, the SLOSS debate looks at the pros and cons of establishing one large habitat versus several small habitats.

species: A group of organisms with a distinctive set of characteristics, such as physical appearance, genetic structure, and behavior, which can be used to distinguish them from other organisms.

species of concern: Species that might need prescribed, concentrated conservation actions, which depend on the health of the populations and degree and types of threats.

supplier scorecard: Processes and tools used to collect data to measure, rate, or rank suppliers.

supply-chain management: Activities that enable the right product to get to the right consumer, in the right quantity, at the right time.

supporting services: Ecosystem services, such as primary production (where plants make their own food), nutrient cycling, and pollination, which serve as a foundation for all other ecosystem services.

sustainability report: A document that provides an overview of a company's economic, environmental, and social impacts caused by its everyday activities.

wildlife corridor: Any space that facilitates the movement of animals between core habitat fragments, with the goal of maintaining or improving the number of distinct species and the health of species in an area.

zero waste: 90% or greater diversion of all discarded resources from landfills, incinerators, and the environment.

Printed in Great Britain
by Amazon